Technology

W9-BTE-584

A Teaching
Resource Book

Integrating

Design

Education

Activities for

Students

Bill Reynolds
Bob Corney
Norm Dale

MAXWELL MACMILLAN CANADA

Acknowledgements

The authors would like to thank the following people for their expertise, knowledge, and assistance in developing and reviewing this resource.

Marietta Bloch, City of York Board of Education; Eva Carter, York Region Board of Education; Pirrko Eager, York Region Board of Education; Jo-Anne Lake, Durham Board of Education; Jean Pillutti of Storytrain; Allan Smith, Peel Board of Education.

In addition, the authors would like to thank the following for their support and encouragement: Skills-OK; The Industrial Training Committee for North York and York Region including: Bruno Conselmann, BC Instruments; Murray Baker, Boeing / Dehavilland; George Betsch, Diecan Ltd; Fred Etherden, Seneca College; The Halton and Peel Industrial Training Advisory Committee and The West Metro Skills Training Council Inc.

The authors would also like to thank the following reviewers: Basil Tomlinson, Carleton R.C.S.S.B.; Dave Eddy, Curriculum and Instructional Services Centre, Surrey, B.C.; Anna Massara, Dufferin-Peel Board of Education; Bob Perrons, Lincoln Board of Education and Liz Janesen, Lanark Leeds Grenville R.C.S.S.B.

Developmental Editor: Jonathan Bocknek

Design and Art: VISU*Tron*X

Maxwell Macmillan Canada
1200 Eglinton Avenue East, Suite 200
Don Mills, Ontario M3C 3N1

Canadian Cataloguing in Publication Data

Reynolds, Bill, 1948-
        Technology ideas : a teaching resource book

Includes bibliographical references.
ISBN 0-02-954154-9

1. Technology – Study and teaching (Elementary).
I. Corney, Bob, 1933-   . II. Dale, Norm.
III. Title.

T65.R48 1993   372.3'58044   C93-094339-2

Printed in Canada

1 2 3 4 5 96 95 94 93

Technology

I ntegrating

D esign

E ducation

A ctivities for

S tudents

Contents

Preface

It is only since the start of the last quarter of the 20th century that technology has explicitly entered the arena of elementary and secondary school curricula as part of the science-technology-society (STS) triad. And it is even more recent that technology has come to occupy a place of its own as a distinct topic of inquiry.

Some teachers were quick to integrate technology into their existing programs, while others are still relative newcomers. However, whether you are a "rookie" or a "seasoned veteran" of technology education, this resource book is for you.

If technology is already part of your teaching strategies, *Technology IDEAS* is a source of fresh ideas and activities to augment your programs.

If this is your first experience teaching technology, *Technology IDEAS* will provide you with:

- information about types and sources of tools and materials;
- suggestions for creating a practical environment to facilitate and implement technological concepts;
- a wide range of enjoyable and challenging problem-solving activities for your students; and
- an extensive bibliography listing books that may serve as sources of information for you and your students, as well as a literature base to provide examples of the use of technology in society.

Either way, *Technology IDEAS* is a valuable resource that will complement the most extensive resource already available to you: the imaginations of your students. They will continually astound you with their ingenious, and often wise, solutions to technological challenges.

Introduction: A Rationale for Teaching Technology

There is a mistaken perception among many education professionals that technology is simply the use of computers, calculators, video cameras, and videocassette recorders—in short, the use of technological *devices*—in the classroom. However, just as reading is only a part of the process of teaching language arts, using devices is only a part of the process of teaching technology.

Technology is the use of processes, tools, and materials to satisfy needs and wants, and to solve practical problems. For example, clothes are a technological invention aimed at solving practical problems such as keeping warm, preserving modesty, or looking fashionable. The desire to solve problems such as these has resulted, historically, in the invention of many technological devices and processes that are used to create clothing. The sewing needle, the loom, scissors, and the spinning wheel are only a few examples of clothing-related technological inventions.

Virtually every human endeavor—from fashioning a flint cutting tool to planting crops to sending space probes to the Moon and beyond—involves the use and an understanding of technology. It is no surprise, then, that technological literacy has become increasingly important, both within and beyond the classroom.

Technological literacy may be divided into four skill sets:

1. the ability to observe and recognize the use of technology around us;
2. the ability to solve practical problems by using existing technology;
3. the ability to solve practical problems by creating new technology;
4. the ability to evaluate the impact of technology on society and the environment.

Teaching technological literacy is similar to teaching language. Students have a natural inclination to use tools and materials to solve problems, just as they have a natural inclination to use language to communicate. As a teacher, you encourage students to explore and discover language through modelling and by providing opportunities for experimentation. The same approach works for teaching technology.

This resource, *Technology IDEAS*, encourages the development of students' technological literacy by illustrating a variety of strategies that can be integrated into existing curricula. It also provides opportunities for students to use tools, materials, and their imaginations to solve practical problems. All students, regardless of their stage of intellectual and social development, have equal opportunities for success in achieving technological literacy. The level

of success largely depends upon three factors:

- the encouragement that you provide for your students to observe and share their ideas about the natural and technological world;
- the opportunities that you give students to experiment with materials and test their ideas; and
- the belief, shared by both you and your students, that they can do it.

The sense of self-worth and accomplishment that students gain from their experiences with technology will be reflected in their other school work, in their personal interactions, and, it is hoped, beyond the boundaries of the school environment.

The Language of Technology

As with any other discipline, technology has its own language—words that have specific meanings in a technological context. Many of the technical terms that students are likely to meet have been adopted from other disciplines, most notably science. For example, the term "simple machine", as well as the names of the six different simple machines, are all common features of books or chapters dealing with the physical sciences. However, technological vocabulary is often as creative as it is technical. For instance, the term "bug", often used to describe a problem with computers or other mechanical systems, was originally coined as a result of a moth being attracted to the glowing tubes of an early computer.

In their initial experiences with technology, students often invent their own words to describe parts or functions of existing devices, as well as those they build for themselves. This should be encouraged. However, students should also be encouraged to add established technological terminology to their vocabularies as is necessary and appropriate, as long as the words don't become a substitute or an impediment to understanding. (If a student can parrot the definition of a hydraulic system, but doesn't understand what it is or how to build a model of one, what's the point?)

In the course of their research for the Activities provided in this resource, students will be exposed to a variety of technological terms, as well as terms from other disciplines—area, axle, circuit, conductor, drag, friction, gear, hinge, insulator, joint, load, mass, span, volume, weight, and windlass represent only a smattering of such terms. You might consider having students create their own, ongoing technology dictionary, listing terms they come in contact with and have "mastered" as a result of further investigation (from you, parent interviews, dictionaries, encyclopedias, or other reference sources). This approach enables students to "own" the terms they need or are curious about, and dispense with those that provide them with little or no assistance.

Special Note

This resource makes only limited use of technological vocabulary, and attempts to explain such vocabulary when it is used. There are, however, three words that are not explained elsewhere: structure, simple machine, and mechanism. As used in this resource, these terms have the following meanings.

Structure: A structure is the organized assembly of materials that are fashioned to create an object or device. This should not be confused with the term "design", which refers to the *way* in which the components of a structure are assembled.

Simple Machine: As is the case in science, a simple machine is any device that consists of either a single inclined plane, a single lever, a single pulley, a single screw, a single wedge, or a single wheel-and-axle. For example, a doorstop is a simple machine, because it consists of a single wedge. Most machines are actually combinations of simple machines. As such, they are often referred to as compound machines. However, to avoid confusion, within this resource they will be referred to as mechanisms.

Mechanism: The term mechanism is used to describe any device that is made up of more than a single simple machine. Therefore, a compound pulley system (one that includes two or more pulleys) is a mechanism, as is a bicycle, which is made up of several different kinds of simple machines.

Metric Usage

Metric unit symbols found in the activities are as follows. (Note that unit symbols are not abbreviations, so they are not followed by a period.)

cm	(centimetre)
g	(gram)
kg	(kilogram)
m	(metre)
min	(minute)
mL	(millilitre)
s	(second)

In some cases in the Tools and Materials lists, you will find references to inches. While not consistent with SI Metric usage, such units do reflect the fact that certain industries in Canada (notably, the construction industry) continue to employ such measurements at this time.

The Design Process

Like the scientific method, the design process is an orderly procedure students may use to solve problems. The design process lends itself to the formation of design teams that bring together students with a range of skills and abilities. Forming design teams will ensure a wide variety of viewpoints for possible solutions, provide an environment in which mutual respect for differing ideas may be fostered, and create a forum in which cooperative and collaborative learning may occur.

To develop self-confidence and competence with solving technological problems, students will need time to experiment or "play" with ideas, tools, and materials. This is a necessary component of the design process, and is the best way for students to gain experience in discovering and/or recognizing, for example, the properties of materials. In fact, abstract science concepts such as "property" or "matter" are more likely to become concrete when students experience them directly in the context of creating practical solutions to a problem.

The table on page 5 illustrates the stages of the design process for three sample Situations. A flow-chart elaborating each stage of the design process appears on page 6. Finally, pages 7–8 provide you with helpful hints for assisting students through the design process.

Outlining the Design Process

The design process developed in this resource involves five main stages:

1. Situation

2. Challenge

3. Exploration and Investigation

4. Choosing and Building a Solution

5. Testing and Evaluating the Solution

Design Stages	Example 1	Example 2	Example 3
Situation	The Happy Hamburger Company would like to eliminate the foam containers that are currently used to keep their burgers warm.	We need to send raw eggs through the mail to the medical research centre.	A new student is coming to our class. She uses a wheelchair.
Challenge	Design a container that will hold a freshly cooked hamburger and keep it warm for up to 10 min. The container must be made of biodegradable materials and be as inexpensive as possible.	Design a container that will hold one raw egg. The container must be able to protect the egg from breaking when dropped from a height of 1 m, must be no larger than 30 cm^3, and have a mass no greater than 100 g.	Redesign the classroom configuration so the new student has easy access to her desk, the computer station, the teacher's desk and the sink.
Exploration and Investigation	Experiment with materials or combinations of materials to see which one(s) retain heat best.	Insert the egg in a shoe box or a tennis ball and experiment with buffering materials that could be used to line the inside of the container.	Create a scale model (2-D or 3-D) of the wheelchair and classroom and its furniture, and experiment with various arrangements.
Choosing and Building a Solution	Build a container using the material or combination of materials that provide the best heat retention.	Line the container with finely shredded paper, place the egg inside, and seal the container.	Use the results of the experimentation to reconfigure the classroom.
Testing and Evaluating the Solution	Cook a hamburger, measure its temperature, then place it in its container and measure the hamburger's temperature again after 10 min.	Simulate sending the raw egg, in its constructed container, through the mail by tossing it several times from student to student, then assess the results.	Borrow a wheelchair and have volunteer students test the new configuration.

Five Stages of the Design Process

Stage 1 Situation
The situation describes the nature of the problem to be solved, or the need to be met.

Stage 2 Challenge
The Challenge is a statement that further defines and focusses the problem described in the Situation. Basically, it outlines a specific task to perform.

Note
At every stage of the process, students should be encouraged to reflect on the expectations of the previous stages to ensure that the Challenge is being resolved. It may be necessary in some cases to revisit previous stages in order to achieve a successful solution. This is known as *feedback*.

Stage 3 Exploration and Investigation
This stage involves brainstorming, research, experimenting, and planning possible solutions to the Challenge. Useful questions to think about here include:

- Are there any existing solutions that already satisfy the Challenge? If so, what are they and how do they work?
- What other solutions might satisfy the Challenge?
- Which of these possible solutions should we explore?
- What techniques, methods, and materials do we need to produce solutions we are exploring?
- What limitations are there in time, materials, size, and cost for the production of these solutions?

Stage 4 Choosing and Building a Solution
The answers to the questions in Stage 3 provide valuable information needed to choose one solution to build. Develop a detailed plan, including the materials you need, the method or procedure you will follow, and any diagrams you have developed to guide you in building your chosen solution. Show this plan to your teacher before you begin construction.

Stage 5 Testing and Evaluating the Solution
Test your solution, using the following questions as a guide:

- Does our solution satisfy the Challenge?
- How does our solution compare with those of other design teams?
- What ways (if any) are there to make our solution better?
- What might be the impact of our team's solution on the environment and on society?
- Does our solution create new, undesirable problems that also require solutions?

Hints for Implementing the Design Process

For Stage 1 (Situation):

■ This should be stated clearly, without bias.

For Stage 2 (Challenge):

■ The Challenge must be specific enough to limit the scope of possible solutions; otherwise, students may attempt solutions that are impractical for the time and/or materials available.

For Stage 3 (Exploration and Investigation):

■ This stage is the heart of the design process. The actual method or sequence of events in which students approach this stage will vary from student to student, and design team to design team. For example, some students may feel comfortable brainstorming ideas right off the bat, while others may prefer to do some researching to discover some initial ideas. Some students may begin by sketching model after possible model, while others may require the security of reference books for specific designs. Precisely how the students proceed is less important than the ideas and experiments they pursue. The following represent general events or activities that will take place (in one form or another) during this stage.

■ Generating Ideas (Brainstorming): Brainstorming is an essential component of problem solving. It draws upon the experiences and ideas of team members, and stimulates thought around the Challenge. Brainstorming may involve words, sketches, pictures from reference materials, or a combination of these three. The main goal is to list as many different ideas as possible that might satisfy the Challenge. Details can be developed later, since quantity is the initial aim. All team members should submit and accept ideas without judgement. Some of the most outrageous thoughts often stimulate new, creative ideas.

■ Research: Students can begin to flesh out (or find) their ideas by consulting a variety of reference sources. The depth of research will depend on their ages and the facilities available within the school or community. At the least, students should be able to discover existing technological solutions to the Challenge. Sketching their ideas is often helpful, since pictures may reveal limitations or difficulties that aren't immediately evident with words alone. Sketches may also stimulate further ideas for solutions. Eventually, design team members should select the idea or ideas that look most promising for responding to the Challenge. Time constraints will determine the number of ideas that students can efficiently focus on.

■ Often a solution will require students to investigate the properties of materials or mechanisms to determine if they are suitable for their plans. In this sense, Stage 3 is a close kin to the scientific method of inquiry, and may involve the need for fair testing.

■ It is important that students remain focussed on the Challenge during this stage. Often they become enthralled with some aspect of their investigations and forget their goal. This isn't cause for alarm, necessarily, because side-tracks of this sort often produce "teachable moments". For example, if students become fascinated with mechanisms such as syringe-hydraulics or electric buzzers for their own sake, they are demonstrating interests that you can refocus to illustrate scientific and/or mathematical principles. Be prepared to "seize the moment" when it occurs; students can always return to the Challenge afterward.

For Stage 4 (Choose and Build):

■ Students should ask you to review and approve the plans for their chosen solution before they begin constructing it. This gives you an opportunity to troubleshoot in case you see a design flaw the students haven't considered or the potential for danger. Some students may exhibit greater skills or experience during this stage. Encourage them to develop their skills, but reinforce the need for all members of the design team to participate so they, too, can gain experience. Constructing the solution must be a team effort.

For Stage 5 (Testing and Evaluating):

- Students should review the Challenge to evaluate their solution. It is important to remind students that, in technology, there are no "right" answers; there are only better solutions. The evaluation may help them discover improvements. If time allows, encourage students to modify their designs and implement their improvements. This stage could be carried out as a competition or a display of products developed by different design teams. Alternatively, students could be asked to "market" their products by making an advertisement to sell their solution to the class. This approach, because it requires students to emphasize the most unique or salient features of their designs, integrates naturally with media literacy initiatives.

- Regardless of the approach used for solution evaluation, encourage students to reflect on their personal discoveries by asking themselves questions such as:
  - What have I learned about technology?
  - What have I learned about the design process?
  - What have I learned about myself that I didn't know before?

A Note about Record-Keeping

Each design team should maintain some record of the design process, for the students' benefit as well as for your own. (See "Evaluating Technology Activities" in the section entitled Technology Activities.) A design folder is one method of record-keeping you might employ. The folder could include any or all of the information in the diagram below.

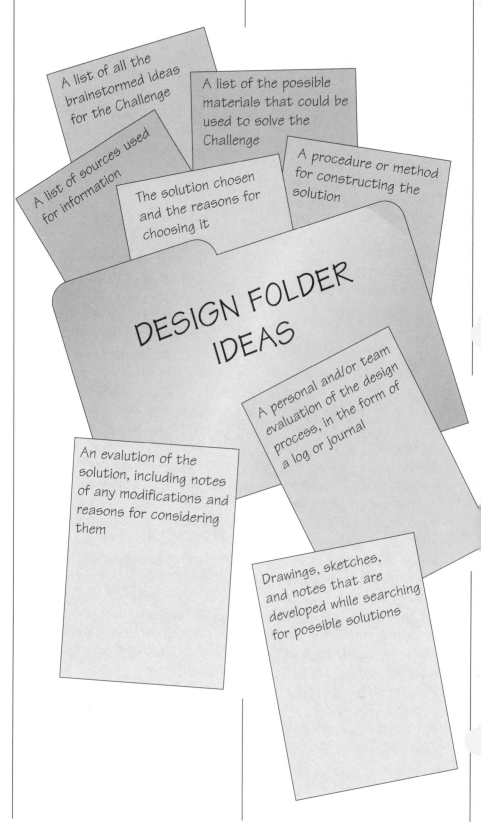

A list of all the brainstormed ideas for the Challenge

A list of the possible materials that could be used to solve the Challenge

A list of sources used for information

The solution chosen and the reasons for choosing it

A procedure or method for constructing the solution

DESIGN FOLDER IDEAS

A personal and/or team evaluation of the design process, in the form of a log or journal

An evaluation of the solution, including notes of any modifications and reasons for considering them

Drawings, sketches, and notes that are developed while searching for possible solutions

Getting Ready

By establishing several dedicated spaces in your classroom (or in several classrooms) as work stations, and by equipping each station with some basic tools and materials, you are well on your way to turning your classroom into a technology resource centre.

What follows are outlines and ideas for creating three kinds of student work areas, or stations: the Unbuilding Station, the Modelling Station, and the Constructing Station. These are suggestions only, to help you visualize what a "technology classroom" might look like, and how it might operate. Depending on the space you have available, and your experience with technology education, you might want to combine some or all of these stations together.

The Unbuilding Station

This station provides space for students to dismantle old or broken toys and small appliances, and to sort and store the various unbuilt parts and components for future use in technology projects. The station may also be a source of materials for science activities, as well as for junk-art sculptures or multimedia collages.

Materials to Unbuild: Preparation for the Unbuilding Centre should begin as early as possible. Sending a letter home with students may yield the best variety and quantity of old, broken, or unwanted items such as toaster ovens, blenders, wind-up or battery-operated toys, sprinklers, and flashlights.

Tools for Unbuilding: A basic "tool kit" is outlined below. Depending on the number and variety of tools you have available, you could keep them either here or in the Constructing Station (see page 11).

More detailed information about types of tools and how to use them appears in the section of this resource entitled "Tools and Techniques."

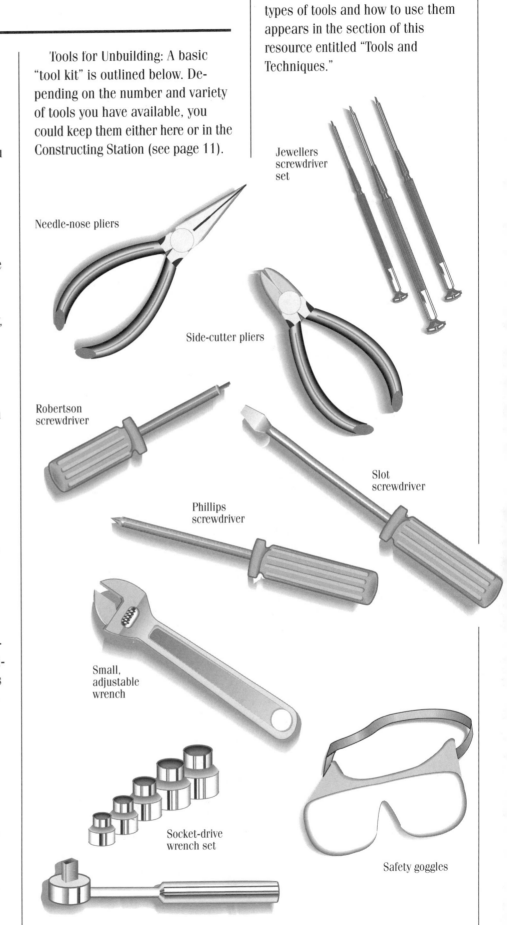

Jewellers screwdriver set

Needle-nose pliers

Side-cutter pliers

Robertson screwdriver

Slot screwdriver

Phillips screwdriver

Small, adjustable wrench

Socket-drive wrench set

Safety goggles

Classifying and Storing Unbuilt Parts and Components: A plentiful supply of plastic containers such as yogurt or margarine tubs is useful for sorting and storing. Encourage students to develop their own classification system. If they need assistance, you might provide one or two examples from the following sample scheme.

Electrical–Electronic Devices

Mechanical Devices

Fastening Devices

Operating Devices

Case Components

Unknown Things

Over the course of the year, as students develop greater skills and knowledge, they may find that their initial classification system no longer suits their needs. For example, students might wish to further subdivide a collection of fastening devices into individual groupings—i.e., one container for screws, another for nuts, another for bolts, etc. Even this scheme could be further

Safety Notes
- Prior to providing devices to students for disassembly, cut the cord caps (the plugs) off any devices that could be inserted into electrical sockets.
- In general, avoid all items that contain picture tubes (such as TVs or computer monitors) or radioactive components (such as smoke detectors). If you have any doubts about the safety of a donated item, discard it.

For current, specific guidelines and directions on classroom safety, consult your local school board or Ministry/Department of Education.

sorted. Take screws. Students might recognize, and reflect in their sorting, that screws come in different lengths, diameters, thread coarseness (the number of threads per centimetre), and head type (slot, Phillips, Robertson, etc.).

However students choose to classify their parts and components, it should be their decision. They're the ones using the Unbuilding Centre, so their system(s) must make sense and be useful for them.

The Modelling Station

Note: This segment describes ideas for incorporating commercially available kits into your teaching of

technology. Such kits are becoming a more common fixture of many classrooms or schools. However, the reality of strained budgets and evolving priorities is that many schools may not have access to even one of these kits. If this is the case facing you, turn to the section in this resource entitled "Creating Structures and Mechanisms."

Many excellent technology kits are available for purchase. Each provides opportunities for different approaches and solutions to various situations, as well as for developing ideas in a concrete, three-dimensional medium that students may find familiar and non-threatening. The kits also allow you to observe and listen to students interacting and experimenting with their ideas in both structured and open-ended activities.

Technology kit manufacturers include Capsela, Fischertechnik, Lasy, LEGO, Meccanno, Sono, and Teko—to name but a few. Many manufacturers produce kits for several user levels, from kindergarten through to secondary. In addition, each kit differs in the materials and accessories provided.

Your best approach to finding a kit that suits the needs of your class (and your budget) is to consult educational supply catalogues and (where appropriate) retail stores that specialize in science and technology products. A technology professional employed by your Board could also be a source of information.

Technology Kits As Concept-Builders

Regardless of grade level, all students need opportunities to become familiar with the materials in the kits, as well as to indulge in free, open-ended experimentation. As students create various devices, ask them to describe the operation of their models' mechanisms or to explain why the structures are made up of the parts they have used. Such questioning encourages students to reflect and focus on their discoveries, and prepares them for activities that are more directed.

As students' skills and understandings develop, the challenges they undertake can become more sophisticated. You might ask students to build a model from a set of plans, and then modify the model to perform a specific task for which the plans did not allow. You could also ask students to build models with similar functions and to compare the differences in their designs. Examples here might include comparing different bridges for stability or strength, comparing vehicles with different wheel sizes, and comparing gear-driven systems to pulley-driven systems.

Using kits also helps student gain experience in following pictorial directions. For example, some LEGO kits have activity cards that provide step-by-step diagrams, as well as pictures of completed models with no intermediate stages. With the aid of cameras, students can document their own model construction in a similar way, either by photographing the gradual assembly of their model or by photographing it in its finished form. These photos could be used by other design teams to trouble-shoot or evaluate the models made by other teams.

Following and making use of pictorial information greatly enhances students' observation skills, and reinforces an important idea. In technology, it is important to understand the precise nature of pictorial information. For example, students may have to find out (the "hard way") that substituting parts that are not called for in pictorial directions can make completing a working model difficult or impossible.

Technology Kits As Part of the Design Process

Technology kits also provide students with a medium for modelling solutions to the Challenges for their Technology Activities. Used in this way, the kits complement the Exploration and Investigation stage of the design process described earlier. For example, once students have brainstormed possible solutions to a Challenge, they could use the kits to test the feasibility of some or all of their ideas.

Kits may also be used to create intermediate or prototype models to serve as the basic "plan" for the permanent model they will build at the Constructing Station. It is important to note, however, that in some cases components comparable to those available in the kits cannot be found in or fabricated from the recycled materials at the Unbuilding Station. In such instances, parts from the kits could be integrated into the students' finished models.

The Constructing Station

This area provides access to work space, materials, tools, and equipment that students will need to construct their final product—their solution to the Challenge.

Students, as well as teachers, will come to class possessing varying levels of familiarity with recognizing and handling different kinds of hand tools. The upcoming section, "Tools and Techniques" provides information about the range of tools and techniques that you may introduce to your class. If practical, you might solicit the aid of an experienced colleague or parent to help you; the school custodian may also be able to provide assistance. In addition, those students who themselves have ample experience with carpentry or similar tool use might be asked to help you demonstrate the types of tools available in your class and proper techniques for using them safely.

Tools and Techniques

The tools described in this section are relatively inexpensive and readily available from local sources such as hardware stores. (An exception might be bench hooks, which are, however, easy to make, and directions for doing so are included in this section.) Some parents might also be willing to loan tools for use during the school year; however, parents should be warned of the possibility that tools may suffer scuffs or scratches (or worse) during the course of student use.

Obviously, budgets and the number of technology classes in your school will determine the types and quantity of tools that you have available. Depending on your situation, one way to save on tool costs is to establish a portable technology centre that can be moved from class to class; however, extra tools may still be necessary if two or more classes are working on technology projects simultaneously.

Ideally, each design team would have access to the tools noted below. Detailed information about these tools and techniques for their safe use follows.

Note: In addition to the essential tools, you might be in a position to consider the following optional, "luxury" items: a socket driver set, a work bench, a miter box (used with a back saw to cut on an angle accurately), a C-clamp, an electric drill. Some of these, like the workbench, are quite expensive and may never see the light of your classroom. In any event, these items should be considered optional; none of them is required for any activities contained in this resource.

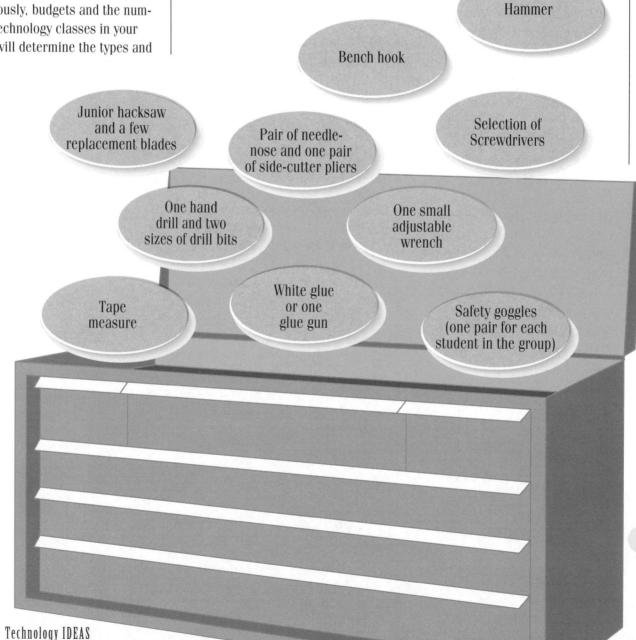

- Hammer
- Bench hook
- Junior hacksaw and a few replacement blades
- Pair of needle-nose and one pair of side-cutter pliers
- Selection of Screwdrivers
- One hand drill and two sizes of drill bits
- One small adjustable wrench
- Tape measure
- White glue or one glue gun
- Safety goggles (one pair for each student in the group)

Screwdrivers

Screwdrivers come in a variety of types. The most common types are shown here. Each is available with different shaft lengths, as well as different head and handle sizes. Regardless of the type of screwdriver, you will probably find that a 10 cm (4 inch) shaft with a narrow-diameter handle suits your needs best.

The following types and sizes are recommended for a class set:
- slot: 3/16 inch and 3/8 inch blade sizes
- Phillips: #0 and #1 blade sizes
- Robertson: #0 (yellow), #1 (green), #2 (red), and #3 (black) blade sizes

- torx: there are many different sizes; you may wish to acquire these as need arises.
- jeweller's set: includes both slot and Phillips types

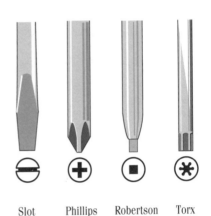

Slot   Phillips   Robertson   Torx

Hints for the Safe and Effective Use of Screwdrivers

- Turn a screwdriver clockwise to tighten a screw, and counterclockwise to loosen it.

Saws

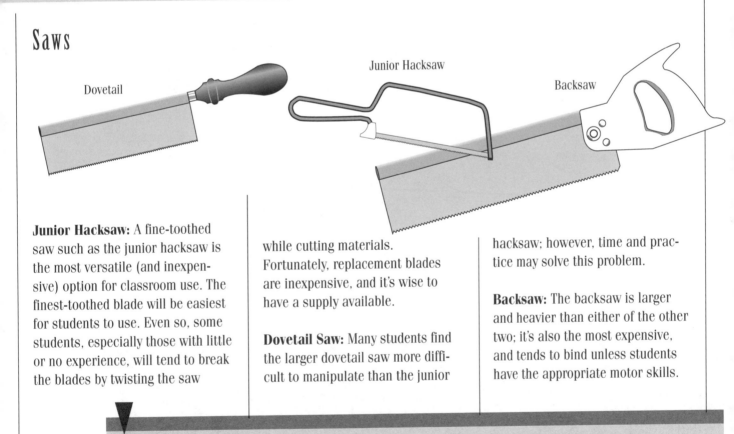

Dovetail   Junior Hacksaw   Backsaw

Junior Hacksaw: A fine-toothed saw such as the junior hacksaw is the most versatile (and inexpensive) option for classroom use. The finest-toothed blade will be easiest for students to use. Even so, some students, especially those with little or no experience, will tend to break the blades by twisting the saw while cutting materials. Fortunately, replacement blades are inexpensive, and it's wise to have a supply available.

Dovetail Saw: Many students find the larger dovetail saw more difficult to manipulate than the junior hacksaw; however, time and practice may solve this problem.

Backsaw: The backsaw is larger and heavier than either of the other two; it's also the most expensive, and tends to bind unless students have the appropriate motor skills.

Hints for the Safe and Effective Use of a Saw

- Each tooth of a saw is a tiny wedge whose job is to cut. Sliding the saw back and forth with gentle pressure is all that's necessary to take advantage of this useful tool. The saw's teeth should cut on the forward movement of the blade. Note also that if too much pressure is exerted on the saw, the blade will bind (get stuck).

(continued)

Saws *(cont'd)*

■ Encourage students to practice making straight cuts. Have them start by using a ruler or measuring tape to draw a straight pencil line. Then they can begin cutting, taking as much time as they need. (It's not a race!) Accurate cuts will pay dividends when building structures, especially those with moving parts. A few millimetres off in a measurement or cut will be amplified to produce a noticeable distortion in the final model.

■ For building more complex structures involving angled cuts, a miter box could be used in combination with a back saw. Some miter boxes are designed for 45° cuts, while others allow the user to select any angle. However, a miter box is not necessary, and should be considered only if students have developed sufficient design capabilities (and if funding allows).

The Bench Hook

The bench hook is an easy-to-make device that makes it possible to cut wood on a regular classroom desk without risk of damage. Another purpose of a bench hook is to keep wood steady while it is being cut.

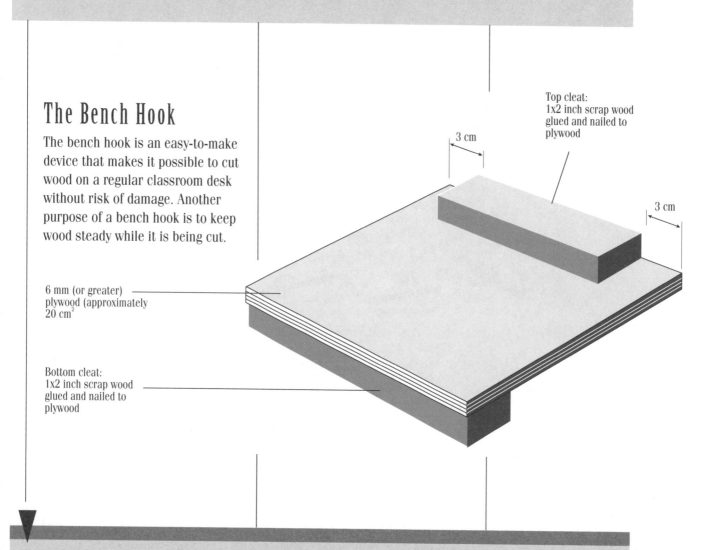

Top cleat:
1x2 inch scrap wood glued and nailed to plywood

3 cm

3 cm

6 mm (or greater) plywood (approximately 20 cm^2

Bottom cleat:
1x2 inch scrap wood glued and nailed to plywood

Hints for the Safe and Effective Use of the Bench Hook

■ The bench hook rests on the top of a working surface (desk or table) with the bottom cleat pressed snuggly against the working surface's edge to hold it steady. (See top of page 15.) The stock (wood or plastic) to be cut is held securely by hand against the top cleat. The thumb is used to help guide the placement of the saw blade, but care is needed to keep the thumb out of harm's way while cutting. If a C-clamp is available, the stock can be held securely against the bench hook with minimal use of the hand.

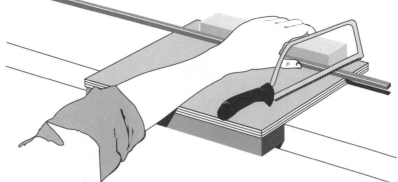

Using the bench
hook and saw

Hammers and Nails

Hammers come in a variety of
shapes and sizes. An 8 oz. claw
hammer suits most students' needs.
Make sure that the hammer head is
firmly attached to the handle.
(Wooden hammer handles sometimes become loose, and the head
could fly off.)

The visible difference between
common nails and finishing nails is
the size of their heads. Common
nails are also easier to
drive than finishing nails.
When driving either kind of
nail, wood should be placed

on a piece of scrap lumber to prevent damage to desks or tables.

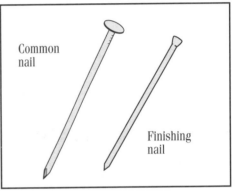

Common
nail

Finishing
nail

Hints for the Safe and Effective Use of Hammers and Nails

■ Holding the handle as close to the end as
possible allows the user to strike nails
with considerable force. Younger or inex-
perienced students may tend to "choke"
the hammer (grip it close to the head) in
order to hit the nails on the head more
accurately, even though they will not be
able to generate as much force for ham-
mering. This is not critical, however, and it
may save a few bruised fingers or thumbs.

■ Safety goggles are strongly recommended, especially if students are working with large pieces of wood and are
driving nails with enthusiasm. Nails can
chip and fly off when when struck with a
glancing blow, posing a danger to the
user and bystanders.

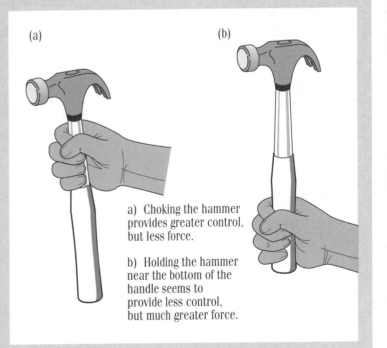

(a)   (b)

a) Choking the hammer
provides greater control,
but less force.

b) Holding the hammer
near the bottom of the
handle seems to
provide less control,
but much greater force.

Hand Drills

Hand drills are safer to use than electric drills, and are almost as versatile, although they require greater manual dexterity. (If money is no object, a benchtop drill press would be ideal.) Two different sizes of drill bits are needed for most work. A 3.2 mm (1/8 inch) bit provides clearance for the bamboo barbecue skewers recommended for use as axles. A 2.8 mm (7/64 inch) bit makes a tight hole for skewers and provides clearance for one-inch common nails and finishing nails that may be used to produce movable joints. Note: If wooden dowels are used for axles, a 7 mm (1/4 inch) drill bit may be required.

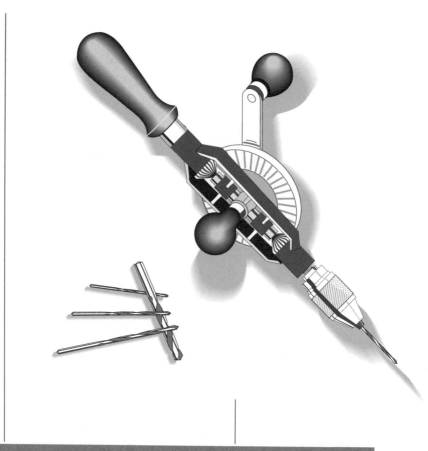

Hints for the Safe and Effective Use of a Hand Drill

- To protect desktops and tabletops, drill with the stock (material to be drilled) jutting over the edge of the desk or table surface. Otherwise, place the material on a piece of wood that is thicker than the length of the drill bit. If a C-clamp is not available to hold the stock in place, two students are needed for most drilling jobs; one to drill and the other to hold the stock steady.

- The drill should be held straight up and still while the handle is rotated. If the drill rocks to the side while drilling, the bit will move on the surface of the stock, causing the hole to become misshapen. If the bit enters a thick piece of wood improperly, any rocking action could bend or break the bit.

- The drill handle must be rotated clockwise. (The bit will not cut if the handle is turned counterclockwise.)

- A starting point for the drill bit can be made by making an indentation in the material with a nail that is lightly tapped with a hammer.

The Glue Gun and Other Fasteners

A glue gun, when loaded with a dry stick of glue and plugged in, heats the glue within five minutes. By depressing the trigger, the glue gun releases the hot glue in a narrow stream; the stream of glue is cut off as soon as the trigger is released.

Since the hot glue dries in about one minute, and since it can be used to fasten many different kinds of materials, glue guns certainly speed up project assembly. However, glue guns are not essential for most work. White glue works well for fastening wood and paper, although it takes time to dry. And duct tape may be used to fasten plastic and metal parts together. (Masking tape is cheaper and does a satisfactory job for temporary or short-term connections; Scotch tape (or any brand of cellophane tape) could be used when strength of the join is not critical, but appearance is.)

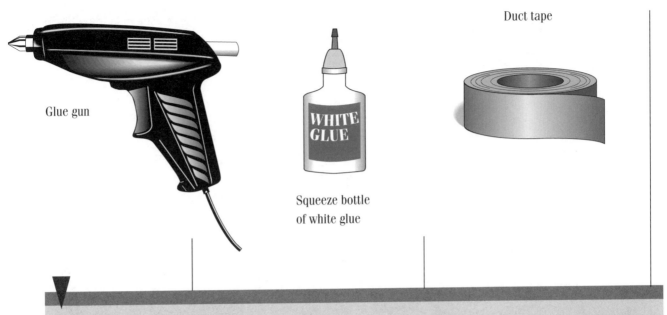

Glue gun

Squeeze bottle
of white glue

Duct tape

Hints for the Safe and Effective Use of Glue Guns

■ Never touch the tip of the glue gun or the hot, liquid glue. In case of burns, immediately run cold water over the affected area.

■ Set up glue guns in a well supervised location. Only one or two students should stand around the glue gun area at a time.

■ When gluing small pieces of material together, use pliers to hold them in order to keep fingers away from the join.

■ A glue gun must be kept upright on its stand when not in use. If the glue gun is left on its side while plugged in, hot glue can back up inside the gun and cool. This will jam the gun and render it useless.

■ Dry glue sticks are available in light, medium, and heavy duty strengths. The heavy duty sticks are recommended for most work.

■ If possible, obtain low-temperature glue guns, which only reach about 125°C. This is still hot enough to cause burns, but is cooler than conventional glue guns.

Creating Structures and Mechanisms

It often helps to "prime the pump" when introducing technology activities to students. Commercially available technology kits provide this form of assistance. However, you may not have access to kits, and some students have difficulty making the transition from manufactured, snap-together technology to material manipulation. This section, therefore, is provided to serve two main functions:

■ to give students discrete, closed-ended problem-solving experiences involving structures and mechanisms; and
■ to equip students with several structures and mechanisms that they may apply to later, more open-ended problem-solving experiences.

Creating Structures

1. Beams

Beam is an Old English word for tree. In today's world, a beam is a length of material (usually wood, concrete, or metal) that is used horizontally to support a load. You can help students discover characteristics of beam construction with the following series of challenges.

(a) Ask students to build a bridge using only a single sheet of bond (typing) paper. The bridge must span a gap of 15 cm, which can be made by setting two small piles of books 15 cm apart. The paper itself may be bent, folded, or rolled. (A piece of tape can be used to seal the paper into a rolled, cylindrical shape.) Students can test which of their bridge design supports the most mass by loading it at the centre with small masses such as coins.

What to Look For: Each design will offer different advantages and disadvantages. A rolled tube of paper is strong, but does not offer a flat surface on which to place a load. Folding the paper into a thick, narrow strip offers strength and flatness, but at the expense of surface area. Making accordion-like multiple folds provides strength and width, but tends to flatten under heavier loads. Students will likely discover that strength depends on the thickness of the beam (paper); folding or bending is one way that flexible and apparently weak materials may be made stronger.

(b) Have students double the greatest load their single-sheet bridge was able to support. (It likely will fail; if not, ask them to increase the load until the bridge does fail.) Then ask them to devise a way to make the bridge support this larger load. The only materials they can choose from are additional sheets of paper, glue, and tape.

What to Look For: There are many ways to satisfy this challenge. Students might try to strengthen the sheet of paper they already have by sandwiching an accordion-shaped sheet of paper between two additional sheets (creating, in effect, a corrugated "board"; the sheets may be glued or taped as they are or folded once or twice lengthwise for greater strength. They might also try gluing several sheets of paper on top of each other to create a thicker beam. Another approach is to support the original sheet from underneath, shaping one or several sheets of paper into arches, columns, or tri-

angles to hold up the beam at its centre. Both of these approaches could also be combined with great success.

A Special Note about Supporting Structures: Supporting, or bracing, structures such as columns, triangles, arches, and domes are so prevalent in the natural and human-made environment that most of us have become immune to their presence. However, even half an hour skimming through magazines or picture books, or wandering around the school grounds, will amaze students with the number of times and ways these simple shapes appear. And they appear with good reason. Triangles, arches, and domes especially are extremely strong, stable structures.

(c) Now have students widen the span (gap) of the bridge to 30 cm or more, until their designs from (b) are no longer able to support a large mass (i.e., until their bridges fail again). Ask them to redesign their bridges so they are able to support the greastest possible mass.

What to Look For: The span here is too wide for a single sheet of paper to span by itself, so students must now find suitable ways to join their paper beams together. Depending on how they do this, you might ask them to consider whether it's glue (or tape) that is contributing strength to their structures, as opposed to the way they design the beams.

2. Making Connections: Fixed and Movable Joints

As noted elsewhere in this resource, students will use glue as the chief means of connecting structures and components for their activities. By its very nature, glue (or similar adhesives such as tape or mortar) provides a way of

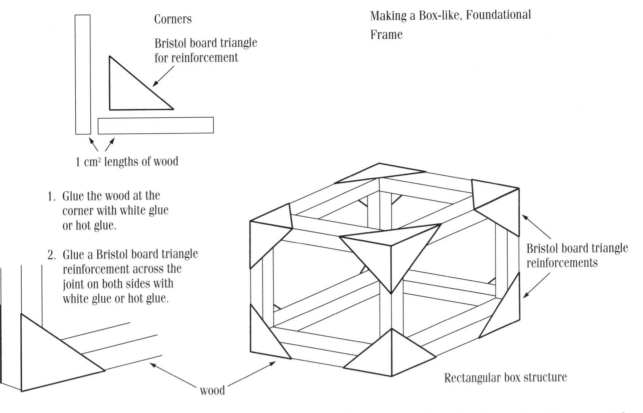

Corners

Bristol board triangle for reinforcement

Making a Box-like, Foundational Frame

1 cm² lengths of wood

1. Glue the wood at the corner with white glue or hot glue.

2. Glue a Bristol board triangle reinforcement across the joint on both sides with white glue or hot glue.

wood

Bristol board triangle reinforcements

Rectangular box structure

"fixing" materials together so they do not move. Nails and screws can be used in the same way.

However, many structures and devices require materials to be joined together, while still permitting movement. Students will require these movable, or articulated, joints to create the machines and mechanisms (such as hinges, pivots, and wheel-and-axles) they need to solve many of their Challenges. These are discussed below under the title "Creating Mechanisms for Motion and Control."

3. Foundations (Frames)

The basis for many projects will be creating a foundation to provide a base structure around which the final project will be built. In the case of a building, this base structure can be likened to the steel or concrete frame that can be seen on most commercial and industrial construction sites. In the case of a car, the base structure can be likened to the frame around which the exterior sheet metal is formed.

An easy and effective foundational frame is the rectangular structure shown above. It is made with wood and glue, and is reinforced with Bristol board triangles that are connected at the intersection of the wood beams; these triangles significantly increase the strength of the joints. These box-like frames can be made in any size and may be combined to produce complex shapes for buildings, vehicles, and machine components. They are, in effect, home-made building blocks.

Creating Mechanisms for Motion and Control

Models with moving parts often provide the greatest satisfaction (and the greatest challenge) for students. As noted above, movable connections include hinges, pivots, and wheel-and-axles. The action may be produced by belts, springs, chains, pulley systems, gears, hand cranks, electric motors, and pneumatic or hydraulic cylinders.

Most technology kits come with ready-made (or easy-to-assemble) movable components; in some cases, they are computer-controllable. However, it's useful for students to see that they have the power and ability to create their own, similar mechanisms. The following ideas are provided to help you provide direction in this area to students.

1. Wheel-and-Axle

Wheels are easily made from materials such as the lids of jars or plastic containers, thread spools, and pop cans. Axles are also readily available in the form of pencils, pen casings, barbecue skewers, knitting needles, wooden dowels, wire coat hangers, and drinking straws. There are many ways to attach wheels to axles. Two are shown on page 20. In any case, there is always friction between the stationary part and the rotating part. For wheels to turn relatively freely, friction must be minimized (usually by using a lubricant of some sort).

An alternative to using found

items for wheels is for students to make their own from scratch. This gives them greater flexibility and control in designing their particular devices. The technique, shown below, may also be used to create pulley wheels, and (with some thought) can be extended into making gears. The wheels are cut from Bristol board, and the centre of each disk must be known if the axle hole is to be drilled accurately.

Making a Wheel

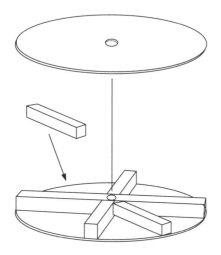

1. Glue spokes on a circle of Bristol board. One spoke should be the full diameter of the circle.

2. Glue a second circle on top of the spokes to complete the wheel.

Using a Home-made Wheel to Construct a Pulley

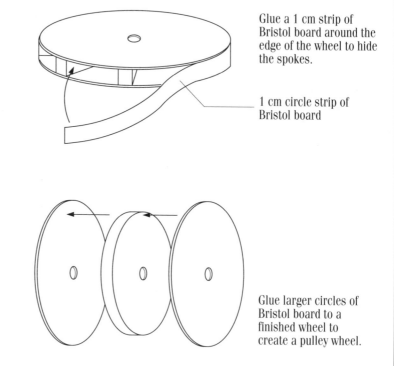

Glue a 1 cm strip of Bristol board around the edge of the wheel to hide the spokes.

1 cm circle strip of Bristol board

Glue larger circles of Bristol board to a finished wheel to create a pulley wheel.

Fixed Wheel and Rotating Axle

In this case, the wheels will roll easily if the axle is attached at their centre. Finding the centre of a circle could be used as a problem-solving activity for students, if that is appropriate. One way is to trace the wheel onto a piece of paper, cut the shape out, and fold the circle twice; the intersection of the folds is the centre. The wheels are bonded to the axle and the axle rotates. For this method, the axle should be placed in some kind of sleeve or held with loosely fitting clips. Barbecue skewers and knitting needles will roll easily inside a plastic drinking straw or the casing of a ballpoint pen. Larger axles will require a tube with a wider diameter.

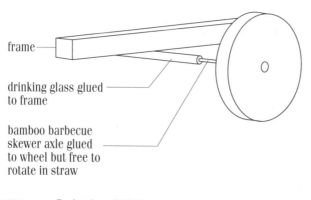

frame

drinking glass glued to frame

bamboo barbecue skewer axle glued to wheel but free to rotate in straw

Fixed Axle and Rotating Wheel

In this method, the axle is glued through a hole in the frame. The hole in the wheel is slightly larger than the diameter of the axle. The wheel is placed on the axle and stands off from the frame by using a spacer. A hub keeps the wheel from falling off the axle.

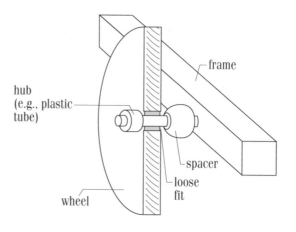

hub (e.g., plastic tube)

frame

spacer

loose fit

wheel

2. Hinges and Pivots

Hinges are relatively simple to make using Bristol board. Fold a rectangle of Bristol board down the centre and glue each half to the parts that are to be joined. Doors or the receptacle portion of a model dump truck may be attached using hinges made in this way.

Pivoting joints, such as those used in a catapult, may be created using nails or barbecue skewers in conjunction with a hand drill. The diagrams show four ways to make these joints.

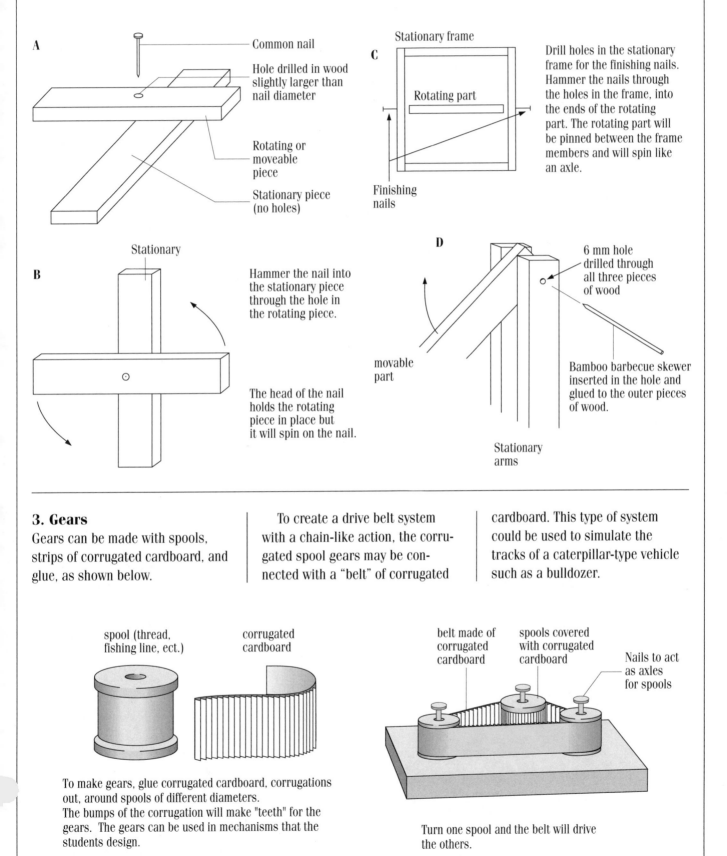

A
Common nail
Hole drilled in wood slightly larger than nail diameter
Rotating or moveable piece
Stationary piece (no holes)

B
Stationary
Hammer the nail into the stationary piece through the hole in the rotating piece.
The head of the nail holds the rotating piece in place but it will spin on the nail.

C
Stationary frame
Rotating part
Finishing nails
Drill holes in the stationary frame for the finishing nails. Hammer the nails through the holes in the frame, into the ends of the rotating part. The rotating part will be pinned between the frame members and will spin like an axle.

D
6 mm hole drilled through all three pieces of wood
movable part
Bamboo barbecue skewer inserted in the hole and glued to the outer pieces of wood.
Stationary arms

3. Gears

Gears can be made with spools, strips of corrugated cardboard, and glue, as shown below.

To create a drive belt system with a chain-like action, the corrugated spool gears may be connected with a "belt" of corrugated cardboard. This type of system could be used to simulate the tracks of a caterpillar-type vehicle such as a bulldozer.

spool (thread, fishing line, ect.)
corrugated cardboard

belt made of corrugated cardboard
spools covered with corrugated cardboard
Nails to act as axles for spools

To make gears, glue corrugated cardboard, corrugations out, around spools of different diameters.
The bumps of the corrugation will make "teeth" for the gears. The gears can be used in mechanisms that the students design.

Turn one spool and the belt will drive the others.

4. Hydraulic and Pneumatic Systems

Any system that works as a result of a force exerted by a fluid in a closed system is called a hydraulic sytem (if the fluid is water or oil) or a pneumatic system (if the fluid is a gas such as air).

Hydraulic systems are at your feet every time you use the brakes to slow down or stop a car. Other common devices that use hydraulic systems include bulldozers, garbage trucks (for tipping out its contents), fork-lift vehicles, and the lift used to raise cars in mechanics' garages. Pneumatic systems are perhaps less common, but examples include certain kinds of drills and the brakes used for massive vehicles such as tractor-trailers.

Syringes and plastic tubing can be used to simulate hydraulic and pneumatic systems. Start by connecting the tips of two empty syringes with plastic tubing. (Rubber tubing, if available, could also be used.) Insert the plunger of one syringe all the way in. Then insert the other plunger just inside the syringe opening. When you push down on this plunger, the other plunger will push out. Voilà— a pneumatic system.

To make a hydraulic system, submerge all components in a sink or container of water. Pull the plunger out of one syringe to fill it with water. Then fully depress the plunger on the other syringe and connect tubing to both syringes. This hydraulic system works best if no air is trapped inside. (A little food colouring added to the water makes the system look a little more impressive. Note also that this hydraulic model can be a little messy!)

Students can experiment with either system to control the movement of something from a distance. For example, they could attempt to lift the lid of a box, push on a lever, or open a drawer. If different-sized syringes are available, students can experiment to find out what effect this might have on their ability to move loads. (If a smaller-diameter syringe is connected with a larger-diameter syringe, the force exerted on the former will be multiplied on the latter, enabling students to move much larger loads.)

Students could also compare pneumatic and hydraulic systems by pushing on a plunger in each simultaneously. They will discover that the hydraulic system has less "play" and the pneumatic system feels more "spongy" or soft. Invite them to suggest reasons for this difference. (Gases such as air are more compressible than liquids such as water.) Noting this difference, students could also infer devices that might use pneumatic systems and those that might use hydraulic systems. Finally, students could be asked to infer why oil is a more commonly used liquid in hydraulic systems than water. (Oil doesn't freeze as easily, and won't rust any metal parts it comes in contact with.)

5. Electrical Circuits

There is little that students can do in designing their own electrical loads (the component in a circuit that uses electrical energy) or their own electrical sources (the component in a circuit that produces electrical energy). Therefore, most designing with electrical circuits will involve using commercial devices (e.g., bells, buzzers, light bulbs) and commercial sources (e.g., batteries, small generators).

However, when it comes to the arrangements of the circuits themselves, the materials used to conduct electricity, and the methods used for controlling the flow of electricity, students have lots of scope for creativity and invention. To help students begin thinking creatively about electrical circuits, you could invite them to try some or all of the following mini-activities.

(a) Have students use a paper clip to build a push-button that will operate a device (light, bell, or buzzer) only when someone pushes on it. The device must shut off automatically when the pressure on the clip is released.

(b) Have students use a paper clip to build a push-button that will operate a device (light, bell, or buzzer) when someone is not push-

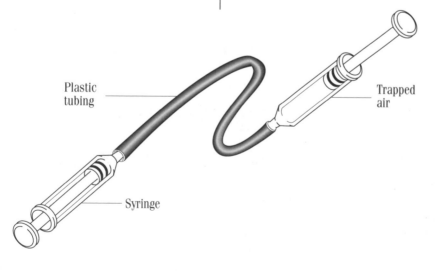

Plastic tubing

Syringe

Trapped air

ing on it. The device must turn on automatically when the pressure on the clip is released and turn off when pressure is applied.

(c) Have students use a paper clip to build a switch that will allow a device to continue operating after the switch is activated. (Such a device is like a common light switch; turn it on and it stays on—turn it off and it stays off.)

(d) Have students make a switch by wrapping aluminum foil around a tennis ball. Roll the ball onto a pair of contacts (e.g., thumb tacks) to complete the circuit and operate a device.

(e) Have students design a switch that will operate by means of flotation. For example, as water is added to a container, the floating switch will automatically activate (or de-activate) the circuit before the container overflows. (Note: If you use batteries as the electrical source, there is no danger from this mixture of water and electricity.)

(f) Have students design a motorized switch that will cause a light to flash as the motor turns a wheel that opens and closes the contacts.

(g) Have students develop a switch that uses the flow of air (through a straw, for instance) to activate or de-activate a circuit.

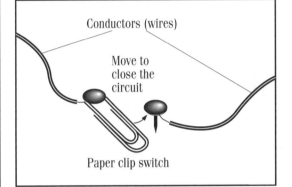

Conductors (wires)

Move to close the circuit

Paper clip switch

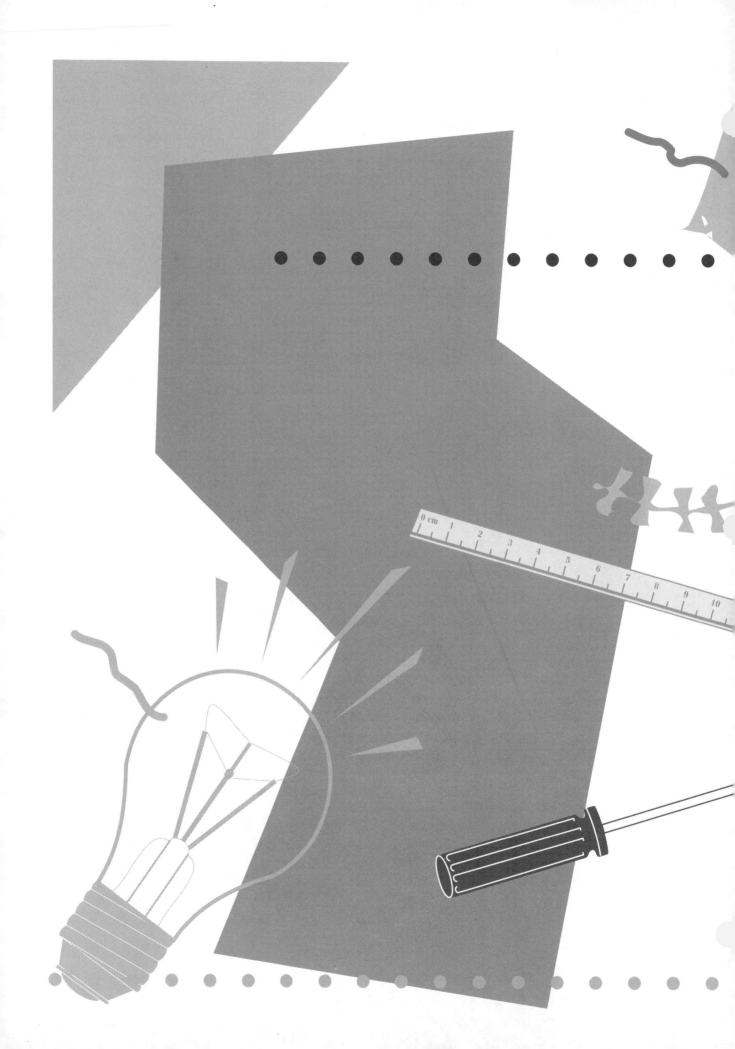

Technology

Integrating
Design
Education
Activities for
Students

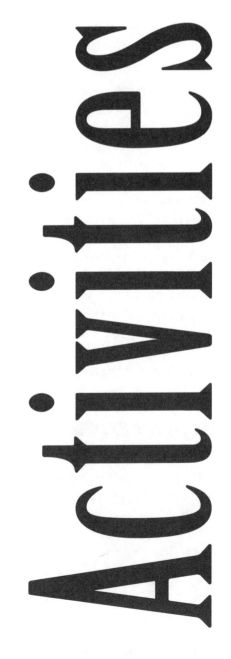

Activities

Technology Activities

This section contains a variety of activities designed to encourage student-centred learning through problem solving activities within the design process. The activities, as presented here, follow a thematic organization. This organization is not intended to be prescriptive. Activities from different thematic blocks may be easily shuffled and/or appended with your own materials to create themes specific to your own needs. It is also possible, in most cases, to abandon a thematic approach and select individual activities at random.

Each activity is self-contained on a single page. The sections intended for the students' eyes—"Situation", "Challenge", and "Tools and Materials"—appear on one side, with Ideas (a selection of practical hints and suggestions for your reference) on the facing side. This approach provides flexibility in the way you present Activities to your students. For example, the student-side of each activity may be photocopied and taped to a student's desk or part of a work station. You could also photocopy an entire theme to be placed in a duotang or file folder. You can even invite students to create their own "Activity Cards" by taping activities to sturdy cardboard; students could also design a container to hold these home-made "Activity Cards."

The following pedagogical processes are offered as guides:

- Students should work in groups of varying sizes.
- Students should be encouraged to discuss the Challenge and plan a solution.
- Brainstorming, research, and experimentation should form the basis of discussions. Students will require time to "play" with the tools and materials in order to test or demonstrate their ideas.
- Diagrams may be produced to illustrate solutions. Diagrams should include dimensions and could, depending on the level of student understanding, be drawn to scale (that is, drawn on a scale of 1:1, which is actual size).
- After group discussion and development of a plan, students should construct their solutions.
- Students should test and, if time allows, modify their solutions.
- Students should evaluate their solutions.

- Students should have an opportunity to present and demonstrate their solutions.
- Students should, in large group discussions, reflect on their experiences in order to synthesize ideas and concepts.

Evaluating Technology Activities

The activities presented here are intended to provide opportunities for students to enhance and reinforce the teaching of the core curriculum, as well as introduce technological concepts, processes, and vocabulary. Since all of the activities integrate several subject areas (see the web diagram on page 27), you will likely employ a variety of strategies to record each student's and design team's progress in the different curriculum areas.

For example, technological tasks usually involve applications of both science and mathematics. You will find ample opportunity to observe and evaluate attitudes, skills, and knowledge in these curriculum areas. Likewise, since group-work is the preferred approach for each activity, listening, speaking, and cooperative and collaborative skills will be practised through all stages of the design process. Anecdotal reports, checklists, videotapes of student interactions for peer-and self-evaluation—basically, evaluation techniques for technology are the same as for any group activity. The addition of design folders or journals can also provide you with opportunities to evaluate written work. (Ideas for design folders were outlined in "The Design Process" section of this resource.)

Note:

The "Tools and Materials" portion of each activity lists items that have proved successful during class-testing and workshops. However, you should feel free to substitute, depending on availability and your own experiences with Technology Education. In addition, while access to commercially available kits is desirable, it is in no way essential. Thus, in those activities where kits are listed in the "Tools and Materials" portion, they are designated as optional.

The key to evaluating technological literacy is observation through the entire process. Avoid linking evaluation to the final product (solution). Instead, look at the process and the approach to solving problems that students employ. Most importantly, evaluation must always be tied back to the original objectives. As a teacher, you determine which of the following is the main purpose of any particular activity:

- the development of good group dynamics;

- the development of communication skills;
- the practice of problem solving strategies;
- the provision of opportunities for student discoveries;
- the demonstration of creativity with technology;
- the demonstration of mathematical skills or knowledge;
- the development of self-esteem;
- the demonstration and development of motor skills.

Certainly, any given activity may give rise to most of these

objectives, but only a few objectives can be selected and adequately assessed at any one time.

Ultimately, the challenge faced by teachers is related to the evaluation of specific technological attitudes, skills, and knowledge. The learning outcomes and their indicators, as found on pages 28-30, are offered as a possible description of a person who has acquired a measure of technological literacy.

This sample web diagram was developed by teachers who attempted technology activities for the first time. It illustrates the variety of experiences that students can enjoy while solving technological challenges.

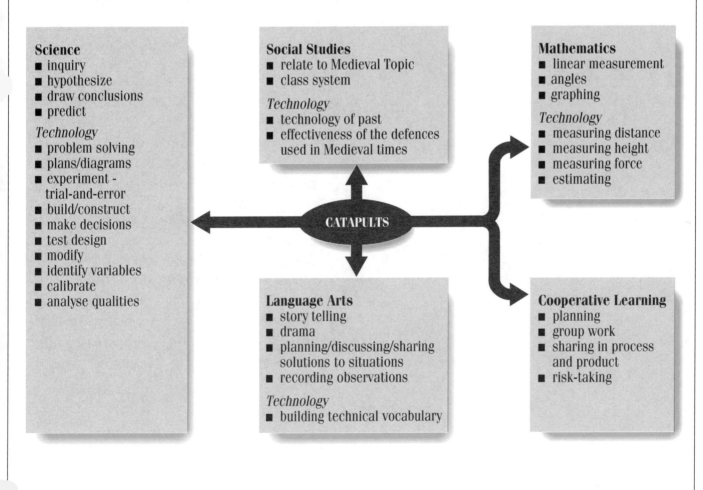

Science
- inquiry
- hypothesize
- draw conclusions
- predict

Technology
- problem solving
- plans/diagrams
- experiment - trial-and-error
- build/construct
- make decisions
- test design
- modify
- identify variables
- calibrate
- analyse qualities

Social Studies
- relate to Medieval Topic
- class system

Technology
- technology of past
- effectiveness of the defences used in Medieval times

Mathematics
- linear measurement
- angles
- graphing

Technology
- measuring distance
- measuring height
- measuring force
- estimating

CATAPULTS

Language Arts
- story telling
- drama
- planning/discussing/sharing solutions to situations
- recording observations

Technology
- building technical vocabulary

Cooperative Learning
- planning
- group work
- sharing in process and product
- risk-taking

Learning Outcomes

Knowledge

The learner demonstrates:

- an understanding of the function of technology and the design process in satisfying needs and wants;

- an understanding of structures and their applications;

- an understanding of mechanisms and their applications;

- an understanding of energy transformations and the efficient use of energy;

- an ability to analyse and critique technological solutions.

Possible Indicators

The student will:

- describe the design process;
- identify needs and suggest the solutions which have been developed;

- identify structural elements (beams, arches, domes, etc.) in existing technology and describe their function;
- use a variety of structures in solving problems;
- use structures appropriate for the given construction materials in the solution of problems;

- identify the elements of simple machines in existing technology and describe their function;
- use simple machines appropriately in their solutions;
- develop mechanisms which rely on the principles of one or more simple machines to operate;

- identify forms of energy and give examples of devices that make use of them;
- analyse forms of energy used in technological devices from an ecological and economic perspective;
- use various forms of energy to design and build technological solutions;

- compare the impact of existing technological solutions to common problems in light of impact on the environment, the economy and society (e.g. automobiles and transportation);
- determine the extent to which solutions satisfy needs;
- propose modifications/improvements to their own solutions and to those of their peers.

Learning Outcomes

Skills

The Learner demonstrates:

- confidence and competence in the use of tools and materials;

- an ability to plan and create technological solutions to given needs;

- an ability to present design ideas in diagrams and words;

- an understanding of spatial sense, properties of shapes and structures, and the ability to translate these from two-dimensional drawings to three-dimensional models;

- an ability to construct devices and structures incorporating one or more simple machines.

Possible Indicators

The student will:

- use tools safely and skillfully;
- select appropriate materials in the solution of technological problems;
- handle materials in a safe manner;
- use measuring instruments appropriately;
- use materials efficiently and with minimum waste;

- describe, model, and develop a variety of technological ideas to solve a given problem;
- analyse and evaluate solution ideas;
- compromise with others to reach a workable solution;
- synthesize ideas from a number of sources into a workable solution;

- present solution ideas in pictorial form;
- illustrate a solution idea from a variety of viewpoints;
- label sketches and diagrams and include dimensions;
- describe with the aid of a sketch or diagram the operation of a solution;

- build solutions from working drawings;
- build stable and workable structures or mechanisms;

- create and/or use one or more simple machines in the solution to the problem;
- use more complex mechanisms such as gears, motors, and hydraulic/pneumatic cylinders in the solution to the problem.

Learning Outcomes

Attitudes

The learner demonstrates:

- consideration and respect for self and others during independent and co-operative and collaborative technology activities;

- the positive attitudes of curiosity, creativity, persistence and initiative;

- confidence in working with technology;

- a concern for the impact of technology and technological innovation on individuals, society, and the environment.

Possible Indicators

The student will:

- maintain a clean work area;
- clean up when work is completed;
- use tools in a safe manner;
- wear appropriate safety equipment;
- share materials and equipment with others;
- listen quietly when others are speaking;
- share ideas with other classmates;

- ask questions about and seek answers to problems;
- modify solutions when unsuccessful;
- use a variety of resources to solve problems;

- use tools and materials creatively while solving problems;
- seek new processes, tools, devices, materials, etc. to solve problems outside of the scope of previous experiences;

- practise energy conservation techniques while working in and around the classroom;
- employ waste reduction practices (recycling, reusing, reducing) while working in and around the classroom.

Medieval Machines

Medieval Machines

These activities suit a medieval theme, and provide opportunities for students to develop an awareness of the craftspeople of the medieval period, the types of work they did, and the contributions they made to castle and village life. These activities may also be integrated with studies such as science, mathematics, music, and drama.

Theme at a Glance

ACTIVITY	STUDENT CHALLENGE
Launch Time!	build a model catapult
Crossing the Moat	build a model drawbridge
Building Barriers	build a model portcullis
Well, Where's the Water?	build a water-retrieval and transportation device

Extensions

1. You could invite students to compare the work done by medieval craftspeople with that of present-day tradespeople. If possible, arrange a tour of a building site to see the various trades at work, and ask students if they can identify any medieval equivalents. For example:

Medieval	Modern
carpenters	carpenters and framers
blacksmiths	sheet metal workers and machinists
diggers	labourers and heavy equipment operators
masons	bricklayers and tile setters
mortar-makers	labourers

2. Ask students to investigate the different kinds of garage doors and how they are related to medieval drawbridge ("Crossing the Moat") and portcullis ("Building Barriers") designs.

3. Invite students to research the structures and technology employed by other, non-European cultures and civilizations during the medieval period or earlier. For example, students might investigate the city-states established by the Mayans or Aztecs, or those of China or Japan during the Middle Ages, and compare their ways of life and the work done by tradespeople with what students have learned about medieval Europe.

Safety Note
Ensure that students know and understand the safe use of hand tools. (Consult "Tools and Techniques" for safety suggestions.)

Launch Time!

Situation:

Your village has decided to put on a circus pageant in honour of the King and Queen, who will be passing through on their tour of the kingdom. The baker will be preparing sumptuous breads and pastries. Lute players and jugglers will be on hand to entertain. Meanwhile, you and your fellow carpenters have decided to amuse onlookers by constructing a mechanism to fling willing participants through the air and into a haystack.

Challenge:

Design and build a device that can accurately launch a large marshmallow so it will land on a target 2 m away. No single piece of wood used in the device may exceed 30 cm. All joints must be glued, and only two nails may be used to make hinged joints.

Tools and Materials:

saw
hammer
drill and drill bits
scissors
metre stick
marshmallows (large)
1 inch nails
1 cm^2 wood (in short lengths)

Bristol board
white glue or
  glue gun
30 cm ruler
bench hook
elastic bands

Ideas for the Teacher

- Students work in groups of 3 to 4.

- Restricting the number and use of nails forces the students to think about how to attach the elastic. Encourage design teams to problem-solve when and if they discover that their device is complete but has no apparent means to attach the elastic.

- The landing area (the "haystack" mentioned in the Situation) could be made from shredded newspaper or waste paper. Alternatively, students could modify the requirements of the Challenge so their target is a waste basket or similar receptacle.

- Encourage students to experiment with their devices to determine improvements they can make. Comparing different devices made by the class should reveal design features that contribute to launching the marshmallow with greater force and accuracy.

- The strength of the joints students create depends upon the accuracy of the cuts they make and the care they take in gluing. A poorly made device will break under the stress of firing the marshmallows. (Historically, such mishaps occurred, much to the displeasure of medieval soldiers.)

Crossing The Moat

Situation:

The Baron has decided to put a moat around the outer castle walls. A structure that spans the moat is required to allow people, carts, and horses to enter and leave the castle. It should also prevent unwanted visitors from entering (or leaving) easily.

Challenge:

Design and build a model for the Baron to approve. For your model, the moat will be 25 cm wide and the doorway will be 20 cm wide. Your solution should support a mass of 500 g. There must be a mechanism that operates from inside the castle to remove the structure from across the moat.

Tools and Materials:

saw	Bristol board
hammer	string
drill and drill bits	spools
white glue or glue gun	bamboo barbecue
scissors	skewers
30 cm ruler	popsicle sticks
bench hook	paint
commercial technology kit (optional)	
1 inch nails	
1 cm^2 wood (in short lengths)	

Ideas for the Teacher

■ Students work in groups of 3 to 4.

■ Provide time for the students to research this project. They will find many ideas in books on medieval castles, and might even be interested in building a model castle.

■ It would be useful if the students had access to kits such as LEGO, Fischertechnik, or Meccano to experiment with cranks, pulleys, and gears. If this is possible, the challenge could be modified to allow the solution to be made from kits alone. This would require less time. Ideally, however, students should make a final model from wood and found items.

Building Barriers

Situation:
The Baron has decided that sometimes it would be nice to leave the drawbridge to the castle down, but still limit access to the castle.

You have been asked to make a model to show how an additional barrier, controlled from inside the castle, could be added to the drawbridge design.

Challenge:
Design and build a model of a barrier to obstruct intruders and which can be operated from within the castle. The doorway through the castle wall is 20 cm wide and 25 cm high.

Tools and Materials:

saw
hammer
drill and drill bits
white glue or glue gun
scissors
30 cm ruler
bench hook
commercial technology kit
    (optional)
1 inch nails
1 cm² wood (in short lengths)

Bristol board
string
spools
bamboo barbecue
    skewers
popsicle sticks
paint

Ideas for the Teacher

- Students work in groups of 3 to 4.

- Provide time for students to research this project. They will find a number of ideas in books on medieval castles. The most likely solution is a portcullis (a sliding gate that can move up and down). A windlass or pulley could be used to raise the portcullis.

- The barrier may be constructed of popsicle sticks or from 1 cm^2 pine strips. It could be painted to look like iron if students wish.

- It would be useful if the students had access to kits such as Lego, Fischertechnik, or Meccano to experiment with cranks, pulleys, and gears. If this is possible, the challenge could be modified to allow the solution to be made from kits alone. This would require less time. Ideally, however, they should make a final model from wood and found items.

Well, Where's the Water?

Situation:
For defensive reasons, a Baronness had her castle built high on a hill. Unfortunately, the source of water for the castle is a well located outside the castle, at the bottom of the hill.

Challenge:
Design and build a device that will lift a bucket of water from the well, and devise a way to transport the water to another location.

Tools and Materials:

saw	Bristol board
hammer	string
drill and drill bits	spools
white glue or glue gun	straws
scissors	plastic containers
30 cm ruler	popsicle sticks
bench hook	bamboo barbecue skewers
commercial technology kit (optional)	
1 inch nails	
1 cm² wood (in short lengths)	

Ideas for the Teacher

■ Students work in groups of 3 to 4.

■ Provide time for students to research this project. There are
many possible solutions. Some ideas may be found by investigat-
ing cultures that have developed around simple, less energy-
demanding technologies than we use in Canada today.

Look at Time

An Alarming

An Alarming Look at Time

These activities suit any topics involving the measurement of time, and may be integrated with studies such as astronomy, social studies, and units of measurement. Students will be experimenting with a variety of materials to design devices that can be used as alarms and/or to keep track of time.

Theme at a Glance

ACTIVITY	STUDENT CHALLENGE
An Alarming Predicament	build an alarm to warn if water rises too far
The Shadow Knows!	build a device that uses the sun to tell time
Eggs-Actly!	build an accurate 3 min timer
It's Your Move	build a timer that will set off an alarm after 60 s

Special Note about Tools and Materials

The Activities, "An Alarming Predicament", "Eggs-Actly!", and "It's Your Move", call for plastic containers. A wide range of such containers is best for students to choose from, including yogurt tubs, peanut butter jars, ice cream buckets, dish detergent squeeze bottles, vinegar bottles, and 35 mm film containers.

The Activities, "An Alarming Predicament" and "It's Your Move", call for aluminum cans. Again, a wide range for students to choose from is best, including pop cans, juice cans, soup cans, bean cans, etc.

Extensions

1. Call and arrange a visit to one of the following: a security firm or a local police public relations office for a speaker who can describe, and possibly demonstrate, some modern security technology; a local bank manager to see about a possible tour of the bank's security systems; a sports arena to observe the timing and score-recording equipment.

2. Challenge students to find as many different timing devices in their homes as possible.

Safety Note
Ensure that students know and understand the safe use of hand tools. (Consult "Tools and Techniques" for safety suggestions.)

An Alarming Predicament

Situation:
Your home is located in a wet area where water from the ground leaks into the basement. An electric pump, located in a pit in the basement floor, pumps water out before it reaches the floor level. If the electric power goes out or if the pump motor fails, the water level may rise and damage the food stored in the basement.

Challenge:
Design and construct an alarm system that will warn you if the water level rises beyond a safe level.

Tools and Materials:

hammer
drill and drill bits
1 cm^2 wood (short lengths)
plastic containers
barbecue skewers
duct tape
marbles
aluminum foil
elastic bands
electric bell or buzzer
paper clips

saw
white glue or glue gun
popsicle sticks
brass fasteners
aluminum cans
insulated electrical
   wire (#22 AWG)
thumb tacks
string
batteries

Ideas for the Teacher

■ Students work in groups of 3 to 4.

■ Provide an opportunity for students to experiment with materials to develop some sort of noise-maker for the alarm. One example might be marbles dropping into a can.

■ The use of an electric-powered alarm is optional. Students may use electric bells or buzzers if they are familiar with electric circuits or as part of a unit on current electricity.

■ Encourage students to think about a triggering mechanism that operates by floating, as in a toilet or a humidifier. This is the key to the most successful solutions.

■ Pop cans have a film of enamel (an insulator) covering the metal to prevent aluminum from contaminating the contents. If the cans are to be used as part of an electric circuit, the enamel should be removed with sandpaper or emery cloth.

The Shadow Knows!

Situation:
You have been transported back to a time before clocks were invented. Your watch batteries are almost dead and there are no replacement batteries. You must push the return button on the time machine three days from now at 2 pm. In order to get back to your time period, you need a way to tell time when your watch no longer works.

Challenge:
Design and build a device that uses the sun to tell the time.

Tools and Materials:
hammer	saw
drill and drill bits	white glue or glue guns
1 cm² wood (short lengths)	popsicle sticks
straws	brass fasteners
barbecue skewers	tape
Bristol board	

Ideas for the Teacher

■ Students work in groups of 2 to 3.

■ Many students try to solve this Challenge without thinking about where, or even when, shadows fall. Group discussions may help students to consider the movement of the sun in the sky.

■ There are several types of sun clocks, including the vertical sun dial and Egyptian sun ladder. Encourage students to research different sun clock designs.

■ Students frequently assume that the sun clock (especially the sun dial) is calibrated like a modern clock, with the 12 hour numbers encircling the centre of a dial. It may take some time before they find that this solution is inadequate, and that they need to calibrate their sun clocks outdoors, in the sun, not in the classroom.

■ Since the sun clock must be located outside, students might also consider designs that protect it from wind and precipitation.

Eggs-Actly!

Situation:

You have been stranded on a deserted island. You have a stopwatch, some sticky tape, and some hand tools. Your stopwatch was damaged in the water and won't work for much longer. Some plastic containers have been washed ashore, and the island has a plentiful supply of clay, reeds, and bamboo stalks. Your favourite food is soft-boiled gull eggs and the eggs are plentiful.

Challenge:

Design and build a device that can accurately time a three-minute soft-boiled egg.

Tools and Materials:

hammer	saw
drill and drill bits	white glue or glue gun
1 cm² wood (short lengths)	funnels
drinking straws	popsicle sticks
barbecue skewers	brass fasteners
duct tape	stopwatch
Plasticine	plastic tubing or trough- like plastic moulding

Ideas for the Teacher

■ Students work in groups of 3 to 4.

■ Timers can be made using sand or water in combination with large plastic containers such as large-size margarine tubs or drinking cups. Have students research sand and water clocks for ideas. (Most students will drill or punch holes in the plastic containers to let sand or water leak out at a constant rate.)

■ Marbles can be used for pebbles. Plastic tubing or trough-like plastic mouldings (from building supply stores) can be used for bamboo stalks. Plasticine can be used for clay. Drinking straws can be used for reeds.

■ The "bamboo stalks" could be used as ducts, raceways, or troughs.

It's Your Move

Situation:
You are playing a word-scramble game with some friends. Each player has 1 min to find as many words as possible with the letters provided. An hourglass-type egg timer comes with the game, and has enough sand in it to last 1 min when it's turned over. Unfortunately, everyone gets so engrossed with the game that nobody watches the timer. As a result, some players get more than 1 min to find their words.

Challenge:
Design and construct a device that will set off an alarm automatically after 1 min.

Tools and Materials:

hammer	saw
drill and drill bits	1 cm² pine (short lengths)
pliers	aluminum foil
white glue or glue gun	funnels
plastic containers	popsicle sticks
drinking straws	brass fasteners
barbecue skewers	stopwatch
duct tape	insulated electrical wire
batteries	(#22 AWG)
bell or buzzer	thumb tacks
aluminum cans	marbles

Ideas for the Teacher

■ Students work in groups of 3 to 4.

■ Students may need to review electric circuits, conductors, and switches if they wish to use an electric bell. They may be encouraged to design a mechanical alarm, instead.

■ Solutions from the Eggs-Actly challenge may be used here, also, but the timer must cause some action to set off the alarm.

■ A stopwatch or similar timing device will be needed for students to calibrate their timer-alarm devices.

■ Students could investigate floatation in order to design a water-based trigger mechanism. As well, mechanical alarms can be made with aluminum cans and marbles.

■ Timers can be made using sand or water in combination with large plastic containers such as large-size margarine tubs or drinking cups, since students may drill or punch holes in the plastic containers to let sand or water leak out at a constant rate.

■ Pop cans have a film of enamel (an insulator) covering the metal to prevent aluminum from contaminating the contents. If the cans are to be used as part of an electric circuit, the enamel should be removed with sandpaper or emery cloth.

On the Move

On the Move

These activities complement a transportation theme, and may be integrated with studies such as machines, force, energy, social studies, and the environment. As preparation, suggest that students observe different types of terrestrial vehicles, such as cars, trucks, tractors, and construction equipment at work in their community (bulldozers, front-end loaders, etc.); these activities encourage students to investigate the operation of such vehicles and build working models of them.

Theme at a Glance

ACTIVITY	STUDENT CHALLENGE
The Junk Mobile	build a model vehicle powered by an elastic band
What a Drag!	build a model vehicle powered by gravity
A Moving Experience	build a model vehicle that uses hydraulics or pneumatics to move objects
A Moving Dilemma	build a device that can move an object from one place to another and return to repeat this sequence

Extensions

1. Students could examine the mechanisms (the "workings") of various toys or games such as the Ghost Buster Trap, and perhaps design their own toy or game based on their discoveries.

2. Students could study vehicles such as bicycles, wagons, rollerblades, and skateboards, and investigate how friction has been reduced in these vehicles. For complex machines such as the bicycle, students could be challenged to trace how energy is transmitted from the pedals to the drive wheels.

3. Possible field trips include a visit to an automotive shop at your local secondary school or service station, or a guided tour of a farm or construction site.

Safety Note
Ensure that students know and understand the safe use of hand tools. (Consult "Tools and Techniques" for safety suggestions.) As well, you should be the repository of the syringes that students will need to make hydraulic or pneumatic systems. Keep close tabs on the syringes to ensure that none leave the classroom.

The Junk Mobile

Situation:

You are the character Gulliver in the novel, *Gulliver's Travels*. Your ship recently set ashore in a land where everyone is a giant and you are the size of a baby mouse. One day, as you were hitching a ride in the back pocket of a friend, you accidently fell out and landed in a small heap of garbage. It's a long trek from the garbage heap back to the house of your friend.

Challenge:

Using materials often discarded in the garbage or found in Blue Box recycling bins, build a vehicle that will transport you as quickly as possible across a distance of 5 m. The vehicle will be powered by an elastic band.

Tools and Materials:

hammer	drill and drill bits
saw	duct tape
cutting pliers	white glue or glue gun
assorted plastic bottles	elastics
bamboo barbecue skewers	plastic lids (such yogurt
wire coat hangers	container lids)
pop cans	drinking straws
Bristol board	paper clips
masking tape	Scotch tape
friction tape	scissors

© Copyright 1993 Maxwell Macmillan Canada

Ideas for the Teacher

■ Students work in groups of 2 to 3.

■ Pencils, barbecue skewers, and coat hanger wire make good axles.

■ Students may try to make a large vehicle. They will discover that the mass of the vehicle is an important factor in determining its speed and distance.

■ Care in constructing the wheels is required to reduce friction between the wheels, axles, and bearings, as well as between the wheels and the floor. The lids from yogurt containers, frozen orange juice cans, juice bottles, and jam jars make excellent wheels.

■ Friction tape may be useful to increase the traction of the vehicle on smooth slippery floors.

■ A twisted elastic band may be used to power a propeller or to turn the axle and drive the wheels. Students should be encouraged to experiment to determine if more elastic bands will improve the vehicle's operation.

What a Drag!

Situation:

A group of students from another school have challenged your class to a Mini-Soapbox Derby.

Challenge:

Design a vehicle that will roll down a ramp from a height of 40 cm and travel as far as possible before stopping. The finished vehicle must be small enough to fit in a shoe box.

Tools and Materials:

hammer

saw

cutting pliers

assorted plastic bottles

lubricants

drinking straws

Bristol board

masking tape

duct tape

pop cans

drill and drill bits

scissors

white glue or glue gun

wire coat hangers

container lids

bamboo barbecue
   skewers

paper clips

Scotch tape

friction tape

Ideas for the Teacher

■ Students work in groups of 2 to 3.

■ The ramp could be constructed from cardboard, plywood, or scrap lumber. Only one ramp is needed for the class. If, however, each group would prefer to make its own ramp, encourage students to think about how to keep their tests fair.

■ Pencils, barbecue skewers, and coat hanger wire make good axles.

■ Care in constructing the wheels and axles is required to reduce friction between the wheels, axles, and bearings. The lids from yogurt containers, frozen orange juice tins, juice bottles, and jam jars make excellent wheels.

■ Students could experiment with different lubricants such as salad oil, butter, and petroleum jelly.

■ Design teams may wish to modify the challenge to compete for speed records.

■ Timing devices and/or starting mechanisms can be developed for competitions.

A Moving Experience

Situation:
You are the chief toy designer for a major toy manufacturer. The president of the company has asked for a new line of toys that have moving parts operated by hydraulic or pneumatic systems.

Challenge:
Using syringes and plastic tubing for the operating mechanisms, design and build a toy vehicle to include hydraulic or pneumatic cylinders. These will lift or move some part of the vehicle.

Tools and Materials:

hammer
saw
cutting pliers
bamboo barbecue skewers
paper clips
Scotch tape
plastic tubing
masking tape
1 cm^2 wood in assorted
  lengths

drill and drill bits
scissors
white glue or glue gun
wire coat hangers
Bristol board
drinking straws
15 mL - 35 mL syringes
  (disposable)

Ideas for the Teacher

■ Students work in groups of 2 to 3.

■ Students should research the operation of farm equipment and construction vehicles that use hydraulic cylinders for such purposes as lifting, pushing, dumping, or digging.

■ Pencils, barbecue skewers, and coat hanger wire make good axles.

■ A model of a pneumatic system can be made by connecting the narrow ends of two syringes together with a length of 3.5 mm ID (internal diameter) plastic tubing. (The tubing fits snugly over the syringes, so no glue or tape is required.)

A Moving Dilemma

Situation:

A loading company needs a way to move steel drums from the warehouse floor to the loading bay area. Your school has been asked to submit designs for consideration.

Challenge:

Design and build a model of a device that is able to lift a cannister and move it over a distance of at least 20 cm. The device (or part of it) must be able to return to the original location to pick up a second cannister. The longest piece of wood in the model should not exceed 30 cm.

Tools and Materials:

hammer	drill and drill bits
saw	scissors
cutting pliers	white glue or glue gun
bamboo barbecue skewers	wire coat hangers
paper clips	Bristol board
scotch tape	drinking straws
6 mm plastic tubing	15 mL - 35 mL syringes (disposable)
masking tape	
string	1 cm^2 wood in assorted lengths
plastic or paper tubes or 35 mm film containers	1 inch common nails
elastic bands	

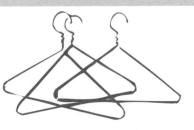

Ideas for the Teacher

■ Students work in groups of 2 to 3

■ Make the containers from 35 mm film cannisters or, if not available, from paper or plastic tubes.

■ Have the students consider the number of different movements that are required to grab, lift, and relocate the container. If students decide to use a hydraulic or pneumatic system for their solution, one syringe system is required for each movement and a minimum of three sets will be required. Alternatively, valves can be installed to control the flow of air or water to the cylinders (syringes).

■ A model of a pneumatic system can be made by connecting the narrow ends of two syringes together with a length of 3.5 mm ID (internal diameter) plastic tubing. (The tubing fits snugly over the syringes, so no glue or tape is required.) When the plunger of one of the syringes is pushed in, the trapped air forces the other syringe plunger to move out. Conversely, when the plunger of one of the syringes is pulled out, the other plunger will be pulled in. If a liquid is trapped inside the syringes and tubing, instead of air, the system is then termed hydraulic. (Refer to "Tools and Techniques, earlier in this resource, for further information.)

Up, Up, and Away

Up, Up, and Away

These activities suit a transportation or flight theme, and may be integrated with studies of machines, force, energy, and/or social studies. As a preparation, suggest that students observe devices that move in air, including airplanes, hot-air and helium-filled balloons, the Space Shuttle, and kites. These observations can be brainstormed with the class before beginning any activities.

Theme at a Glance

ACTIVITY	STUDENT CHALLENGE
Just Dropping In	design a device to lower a load gently
A Banner Day	design a floating banner, without helium
Catching the Breeze	build a model glider
To (Fris)Bee or Not to (Fris)Bee	design a toy that floats or spins in air

Extensions

1. Students might be interested in researching the Gossamer Condor, an ultralight, human-powered aircraft.

2. Arrange a field trip to a local airport where, perhaps, a ground-school instructor or pilot could discuss factors involved in keeping airplanes aloft.

3. Many communities have model airplane clubs or ballooning clubs. A representative could be invited to share stories with the class.

4. Depending on your location, you may be able to arrange a tour of an aircraft museum.

Safety Note
Ensure that students know and understand the safe use of hand tools. (Consult "Tools and Techniques" for safety suggestions.)

Just Dropping In

Situation:
A neighbouring school has challenged your class to an egg-drop contest. The students there claim that they can drop an egg to the ground without breaking it.

Challenge:
Design a device that will allow a raw egg to fall as slowly as possible from a height of 3 m. It must land without breaking.

Tools and Materials:
raw egg
Scotch tape
masking tape
plastic garbage bags

string
tissue paper
plastic food wrap
construction paper

Ideas for the Teacher

■ Students work in groups of 2 to 3.

■ The most obvious solution is a parachute. There are many possible parachute designs and different materials may be tested to get an effective solution. However, some students may explore other solutions such as attaching the egg to a glider.

■ Testing may be done in the gymnasium or in the playground. Exercise extreme caution when using ladders. Playground equipment may provide a suitable platform for safely launching the devices.

■ Another solution could be to have the eggs in a container and surround them with shock-absorbing material.

A Banner Day

Situation:
The annual school fair is fast approaching. In the past, each side of an advertising banner was attached to a helium-filled balloon so the banner could float above the school's roof. However, helium is banned from use at your school.

Challenge:
Design a small-scale model to show your Principal how an advertising banner could be floated above the school.

Tools and Materials:

Scotch tape
masking tape
plastic food wrap
Bristol board
plastic garbage bags
1 cm² balsa wood or
   styrofoam strips

string
tissue paper
construction paper
computer paper
marking pens
white glue or glue gun

Ideas for the Teacher

■ Students work in groups of 2 to 3.

■ Kites and hot air balloons are possible solutions. There are many different types of kites and students should be encouraged to do some research and experiment with different designs. For hot air balloons, a blow dryer may be used as the heat source.

■ To extend this challenge, students may be invited to design a full-scale banner to advertise a coming school event.

■ Students could be challenged to invent a way to keep the banner aloft for extended periods of time.

Catching the Breeze

Situation:
A local radio station is sponsoring a model glider contest, and your class has decided to enter.

Challenge:
Design gliders that can stay aloft as long as possible, or that can travel the farthest distance.

Tools and Materials:

Scotch tape	string
masking tape	tissue paper
construction paper	Bristol board
white glue or glue gun	drinking straws
stopwatch	plastic garbage bags
balsa wood	

Ideas for the Teacher

■ Students work in groups of 2 to 3.

■ Testing should take place indoors to keep air movement to a minimum. A gymnasium is a good test area.

■ Use a stopwatch to measure the time in the air.

■ Designing a fair test is especially difficult for this kind of activity. There are too many factors (variables) that students can't control, such as the presence of air currents, differences in air temperature, and the force and method used to launch the gliders. Even so, students could be challenged to carry out this activity as a fair test, as long as they decide which factors they want to vary. For example, they might decide that all the gliders must be built from the exact same materials, and that they will be launched with exactly the same amount of force from exactly the same height. The only factor that can be altered is the shape and span of the wings.

■ As an extension, students could be challenged to modify their gliders to investigate the greatest mass they can carry, while remaining in the air for as long as possible.

To (Fris)Bee or Not to (Fris)Bee!

Situation:
You work for a toy manufacturer as a design engineer. The Frisbee has been patented by a competitor and is selling well. Your employer has asked you to come up with a toy that will compete with the Frisbee.

Challenge:
Design a toy that floats or spins through the air.

Tools and Materials:
Scotch tape
masking tape
construction paper
Bristol board
white glue or glue gun

Ideas for the Teacher

■ Students work in groups of 2 to 3.

■ Most students are familiar with saucer-shaped toys. This challenge encourages them to think carefully about devices that move through the air when launched.

■ Students could be asked to create a marketable name for their inventions.

■ Invite students to investigate other round- or saucer-shaped objects. For example, burrito wrappers make good "soft" frisbees.

■ Suggest a contest to see which new toy travels the farthest or is most easily maneuvered.

Power of the Press

Power of the Press

These activities suit a communications theme, and may be integrated with studies such as language arts, graphic arts, social studies, science, and the environment. Students will investigate printing, packaging, paper-making, and book-making.

Theme at a Glance

ACTIVITY	STUDENT CHALLENGE
Identify Yourself	design a company logo and printing plate
Wrap It Up	design a candy bar wrapper
Green Greetings	design a greeting card made with recycled paper
Pop-Ups	design a pop-up story book for young readers

Extensions

1. Invite a local artist who works with print-making, silk-screening, or any other print technology, to provide a demonstration for the class. A tour of a commercial printing operation might also be possible.

2. Many advertising agencies, publishers, and printing establishments often employ creative staff who design letterhead, books, posters, and promotional material—often on computer. Ask around your community to find contacts who might be willing to visit the class or provide a tour.

3. Invite students to compare and evaluate the various types of containers or wrappings in which consumer items are packaged.

4. Environmental awareness projects and initiatives involving the 3 Rs are obvious spinoffs from this theme.

Safety Note
Ensure that students know and understand the safe use of hand tools. (Consult "Tools and Techniques" for safety suggestions.)

Identify Yourself

Situation:
You have just started your own company and want to create a logo for all of your communication and marketing materials.

Challenge:
Design a logo for your company and create a printing plate to reproduce the logo on paper. The plate will be made from plaster of Paris and should have a raised image of your logo on the printing surface.

Tools and Materials:

styrofoam dishes or trays
water
clean plastic containers
paper
Plasticine or moulding
    sand
30 cm ruler

plaster of paris
stir sticks
paint (poster or acrylic)
paint brush or roller
fine sand paper
pens and pencils

Ideas for the Teacher

■ Students work in groups of 3 to 4, each group representing a company.

■ Students could create a name and product for their company.

■ Students should research and collect a number of different company logos. Large group discussion should highlight the impact of effective logos.

■ Individual students in the group may produce their own logo designs. The group will evaluate the designs to select one company logo.

■ Students should research plaster casting to become aware of the difference between negative and positive images and the properties of plaster of Paris.

■ Students may have to produce two castings. The first would be a negative, or depressed image, of the logo. The second casting would use the first casting as the mould. Coating the first casting with soap detergent or plastic wrap will prevent the second from sticking to it.

■ Printing involves coating the plate with paint and pressing paper onto the plate. Sandpaper can be used to ensure that the printing surface of the plate is smooth.

Wrap It Up

Situation:
The Chewy Chocolate Company needs to design a package for its new candy bar: the JUMBO BAR. The JUMBO BAR is 20 cm x 4 cm x 3 cm.

Challenge:
Design and decorate an attractive package for the JUMBO BAR. It should use as little material as possible but be noticeable when displayed with all of the competitors' candy bars. The label must include the name of the candy bar, its mass, the company name, and a list of ingredients.

Tools and Materials:
Bristol board
construction paper
tape
white glue
paint
markers
crayons
30 cm ruler
scissors

Ideas for the Teacher

- Students work in groups of 3 to 4.

- Students should collect and compare the wrappers of different kinds of candy bars.

- Students should evaluate the environmental impact of different types of wrapping, and use the results of their evaluation to develop their own environmentally respectful package.

- Students could estimate the mass of the JUMBO BAR by comparing similarly sized candy bars.

- Students may invent their own JUMBO BAR recipe and test it.

- Students may test the marketability of their designs by developing and carrying out a consumer preference survey.

Green Greetings

Situation:
A great many trees are cut to make the paper modern society has come to depend on. Recycling paper is one way to reduce the number of trees that have to be cut down.

Challenge:
Create a greeting card using paper that you make yourself from waste materials.

Tools and Materials:
paper towel
blotting paper
cloth
newsprint
waste plant materials such as leaves, grass, and flowers
fine screen (for example, an old pair of nylon panty hose)
wooden frame
absorbent cloth (such as old cotton or flannel sheets
    or blotting paper)
rolling pin (or large plastic pop bottle)
markers
crayons
paint
scissors
blender

Ideas for the Teacher

■ Students work in groups of 4 to 6. Each group will co-operatively produce about five sheets of paper for the cards and will design greeting cards with proper wording.

■ Encourage students to research the production of handmade paper. Newsprint and some cloth or plant fibres, when blended with water, will produce a good mixture for making paper.

■ Flower petals added to the mixture will produce an interesting texture and colour in the finished paper. Encourage the students to experiment with different ingredients to make their paper.

Pop-Ups

Situation:
The Young Author's Society has selected your class to provide reading materials for students in kindergarten classes.

Challenge:
Design a pop-up book that illustrates a story written by one or all the members of your group. The book should include at least three different pop-up presentations.

Tools and Materials:
construction paper
Bristol board
glue
book binding tape (or duct tape)
cellophane tape
paint
markers
crayons
string
elastics
scissors
30 cm ruler

Ideas for the Teacher

■ Students work in groups of 3 to 4.

■ Students should investigate pop-up book techniques and plan the book before beginning any actual construction.

■ The students could present the books to the resource centre for use with early primary students.

On the Waterfront

On the Waterfront

These activities suit a transportation and water theme, and may be integrated with studies such as physical science (force, pressure, and buoyancy), machines, and the environment. Students will investigate the principles behind the operation of vehicles such as sail boats, submarines, rafts, and barges.

Theme at a Glance

ACTIVITY	STUDENT CHALLENGE
Sailing Along	design a boat propelled without fuel or electricity
Prop It Up	design a boat propelled with an electric motor
The Loch Ness Submersible	build a device that can surface after being submerged

Extensions

1. Students could research nautical terminology to find out the meaning and origin of specific terms. (Just what is a "poop deck", anyway?)

2. Students could research the invention and uses of submersible vehicles, including the unpiloted ROVs (remotely operated vehicles) so important for deep-level underwater research.

3. Challenge the class to find out why some kinds of wood, such as balsa, float on water, while other kinds, such as ebony, sink.

Safety Note

Ensure that students know and understand the safe use of hand tools. (Consult "Tools and Techniques" for safety suggestions.)

Sailing Along

Situation:
A local radio station is sponsoring a model boat race. The catch is that electrically driven and fuel-driven motors can't be used to make the boats move.

Challenge:
Design a model water vehicle that will travel as fast as possible without using electricity or fuel to propel it. The finished model should not exceed 20 cm in length and 8 cm in width.

Tools and Materials:

plastic containers	white glue or glue gun
Scotch tape	string
masking tape	paper
plastic garbage bags	plastic food wrap
construction paper	wood scraps
balloons	elastic bands
electric fan	styrofoam plates or trays

3 m length of water-filled
   eavestrough with 2 end caps
   (for testing the models)

Ideas for the Teacher

■ Students work in groups of 2 to 3.

■ Use a section of plastic eavestrough with the two ends sealed as the canal. Fill it with water.

■ Set up the electric fan to blow down the length of the trough for students who opt for sail power.

■ Encourage students to investigate a variety of power options including paddle wheel and air jet (with a balloon)

■ Students experienced with gears could use a commercial technology kit to produce an elastic-powered boat and experiment with a variety of gear ratios.

■ As an extension, students could modify the challenge so that the finished models must be able to carry a load of specified mass (such as 500 g).

■ A stopwatch could be used to time the models.

Prop It Up

Situation:
Many different organizations are concerned about the pollution in our lakes caused by gasoline-powered boat motors. They are promoting the use of electric motors for boats but to date these motors have had poor speed performance.

Challenge:
Design a model boat powered by a battery-driven electric motor. The boat should be designed for speed and be able to support a mass of 300 g. The finished model should not exceed 20 cm in length and 8 cm in width.

Tools and Materials:

saw	drill
sand paper	wood scraps
bamboo barbecue skewers	popsicle sticks
styrofoam trays/plates	masking tape
batteries	batteries
electric motors	drinking straws
white glue or glue gun	
3 m length of plastic eavestrough (with 2 end caps)	
Lego Technic or Fischertechnik gears	

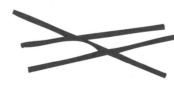

Ideas for the Teacher

■ Students work in groups of 2 to 3.

■ Fill the eavestrough with water for testing design solutions.

■ A stop watch may be used to time the boats and determine their speed.

■ Students should do research into hull design, propeller or paddle design, and weight distribution and its effect on performance, and then apply their discoveries to their design.

■ Students experienced with electricity and gears could use a commercial technology kit to produce a power boat and experiment with a variety of gear ratios.

The Loch Ness Submersible

Situation:

A toy manufacturer wants to create a new toy based on the Loch Ness monster. The toy, called "Nessie", sits underwater and has a mechanism that makes Nessie rise up and out of the water. Your class has been invited to submit designs for a model that will be used to create the Nessie toy.

Challenge:

Design a device that can make a plastic bottle rise and sink as required in a tub of water.

Tools and Materials:

plastic containers   sand
Scotch tape   string
duct tape   dish detergent
balloons   flexible plastic tubing
deep wash tub or sink

Ideas for the Teacher

■ Students work in groups of 2 to 3.

■ Fill a wash tub or sink with water for the testing of the designs.

■ Students may discover that a soft plastic bottle may be used as a syringe to pump air into their submarine through the plastic tubing.

■ Students might like to use their experiences to design and construct a full-scale Nessie toy.

Enduring the Elements

Enduring the Elements

These activities suit a climatological theme, and may be integrated with studies such as atmospheric science, energy, and the environment. Students will be engaged in developing solutions for problems that are for us created by our climate.

Theme at a Glance

ACTIVITY	STUDENT CHALLENGE
Who'll Count the Rain?	build devices to measure weather features
Beat the Heat	design a container to keep liquids cool
Any Way the Wind Blows	build devices to find wind speed and direction

Extensions

1. Invite a meteorologist to discuss weather prediction, forecasting, and the impact that technology has had on this science.

2. Students could investigate the changes that new technology has had on the design and manufacture of clothing—specifically, how natural and human-made fabrics have changed the way people dress for a variety of pursuits (e.g., keeping warm, keeping cool, keeping dry, resistance to wrinkles and stains).

Safety Note
Ensure that students know and understand the safe use of hand tools. (Consult "Tools and Techniques" for safety suggestions.)

Who'll Count the Rain?

Situation:

Meteorologists (people who study and predict weather) need to have accurate information about air pressure, precipitation, and temperature to make their weather predictions. They use instruments that allow them to observe and measure these weather features.

Challenge:

Design and build devices that can be used to measure one or more of the following:
- amount of precipitation
- air pressure
- temperature

Tools and Materials:

saw
hammer
drill and drill bits
white glue or glue gun
scissors
Bristol board
popsicle sticks
markers and/or pencil
   crayons
commercial barometer
   (for calibration)
commercial alcohol thermometer
   (for calibration)

plastic and metal containers
funnels
balloons
bamboo barbecue skewers
30 cm ruler
bench hook
1 inch common nails
tape
1 cm^2 wood (short lengths)

Ideas for the Teacher

■ Students work in groups of 3 to 4.

■ Depending on the level of ability and time available, each design team could work on a different instrument in order to produce a set of meteorological measuring devices. The teams will have to research their task in order to develop a design and plan the construction.

■ Calibrating the instruments is the most complex aspect of the design work. Encourage students to be patient and precise in this part of the task.

■ Students can try keeping records of their instrument findings over an extended period of time. Graphs of the results provide an excellent means of viewing the changes over time.

Beat The Heat

Situation:
On hot summer days, an ice-cold lemonade is a great treat. Unfortunately, the sun soon melts the ice cubes and warms the drink.

Challenge:
Design a container that will help keep cold drinks cold for as long as possible.

Tools and Materials:

paper	cardboard
tape	white glue
styrofoam chips	sawdust
vermiculite	peat moss
salt	refrigerator
plastic containers	alcohol thermometer
lemonade	

Ideas for the Teacher

- Students work in groups of 2 to 3.

- Have the class collect and evaluate a variety of commercially available cool drink containers.

- Invite students to modify or improve commercial products or to invent totally new products.

- Discuss the environmental impact(s) and other aspects of the materials used.

- Have the students develop a fair test to determine the most effective designs.

- An alternative challenge for the winter could be to design a container that will keep hot drinks hot for as long as possible.

Blow Me Down

Situation:
A local model airplane club has expressed an interest in using the schoolyard as the site for a flying show. The club members need to determine wind direction and speed in order to safely take off and land their models.

Challenge:
Design and build devices that can be used to estimate the force and direction of the wind.

Tools and Materials:

hammer	saw
bench hook	drill and drill bits
1 inch common nails	1 cm^2 wood (short lengths)
paper	bamboo barbecue skewers
tape	cardboard
styrofoam cups	white glue or glue gun
cutting pliers	wire coat hanger
plastic shopping bags	drinking straws

Ideas for the Teacher

- Students work in groups of 2 to 4.

- Students should research different instruments used to measure wind speed and direction. It's unlikely that students will actually be able to measure wind speed. (That's why the Challenge is phrased the way it is.) However, their research will no doubt lead to a Beaufort Chart or a similar tabulation comparing visible evidence of wind (e.g., rustling leaves) with a speed range. They may need some help realizing that their designs will have to be based on indirect evidence of this sort. (However, resourceful students with computer experience and electronics know-how may be able to devise a system that can measure windspeed in terms of rotations per second or something similar.)

- A stopwatch could be helpful for timing.

Get the Message?

Get the Message?

These activities complement a communications theme, and may be integrated with studies such as electricity, social studies, computer studies, and language arts.

Theme at a Glance

ACTIVITY	STUDENT CHALLENGE
That Long Distance Feeling	design a simple communication system
Taming Traffic	design a traffic light system
Pass It On	design a telegraph system

Extensions

1. These activities, more than any others in this resource, lead naturally into "high tech" communications—the conversion of information from one form into another. You, or an invited guest, may wish to discuss with the class several different information coding systems such as semaphore, Morse code, Universal Product Code or UPC (those lines and numbers found on most packaged consumer products), American Standard Code for Information Interchange or ASCII (a popular method for encoding alpha-numeric information in binary form for computers). Students could also carry out their own research on one or more of these.

2. Challenge students to invent their own code for general communication or for sending secret messages. You might first discuss the range of non-verbal signals humans use to communicate (e.g., raising hands for permission to speak, knocking on doors, putting a finger to the lips for quiet, a fire alarm bell, a ringing telephone).

3. Arrange a visit by a representative from a phone company to describe the ways that information is distributed, including fibre optics, cellular and microwave systems, and satellite communications. A telephone technician could describe how changes in technology have affected the job over the past several decades.

4. Students could investigate how sound and/or visual images are created by phonograph records, tape recorders, CDs, televisions, VCRs, and facsimile machines. Using any of these devices becomes all the more enjoyable when students understand the "magic" that makes this equipment operate.

> **Safety Note**
> Ensure that students know and understand the safe use of hand tools. (Consult "Tools and Techniques" for safety suggestions.)

That Long Distance Feeling

Situation:
You would like to be able to talk to your friend across the room without having to shout and have everyone else hear you.

Challenge:
Design and build a simple communication system.

Tools and Materials:

cotton string	nylon fishing line
aluminum cans	paper cups
plastic yogurt containers	hammer
drill and drill bits	metre stick
common nails	pliers
(1.5 inch or larger)	
#20 AWG steel wire	
(or any size of thin wire)	

Ideas for the Teacher

■ Students work in groups of 3 to 4.

■ As one of their options, students should build and test a "tin-can telephone system". Students should experiment to determine which material—cotton string, nylon line, or steel wire—transmits sound best, and which transmitter/receiver the paper cup, the steel can, or the plastic cup—functions best.

■ The hammer and nail can be used to punch holes in the can, rather than trying to use a drill.

■ Encourage students to examine how the string (or nylon or wire) may be attached to the receiver/transmitter. A good connection is necessary for the device to function efficiently.

Taming Traffic

Situation:
You are a community planner and are designing and building a model of a small, mountainside village.

Challenge:
Design and build a model to show how a set of traffic lights can be used in the village to control the traffic on the road. They should be designed so that the red and green lights cannot go on at the same time.

Tools and Materials:

batteries	lamp sockets
bulbs	wire
switches	pliers
wire strippers	Bristol board
saw	white glue or glue gun
masking tape	1 cm^2 wood strips
red and green tissue paper	paper clips
thumb tacks	

Ideas for the Teacher

■ Students work in groups of 4 to 5.

■ Students should have had prior experience with electric circuits or be given sufficient time to "play" with the components to make discoveries about circuits and switches. Print resources should be available for their research.

■ Encourage students to solve the electrical switching problem before they begin constructing the traffic lights.

■ Encourage students to make their own switches rather than use commercial electrical switches

■ It is possible to use a computer to control the traffic lights. Investigate the availability of appropriate software and peripherals in your school or Board to facilitate this type of control as part of the student project. Kits such as Lego and Fischertechnik can be used to interface with the computer.

Send It On

Situation:

Before the invention of the telephone, Samuel Morse invented a communication system using electrical signals that allowed people to communicate over long distances. This communication system is known as Morse Code.

Challenge:

Design a telegraph system using switches, batteries, electromagnets, and wires to send a coded message over a distance of at least 30 m.

Tools and Materials:

batteries

lamp sockets

bulbs

switches

wire strippers

paper clips

aluminum cans

sandpaper

magnet wire
   (varnish-coated wire)

insulated electrical wire (#22 AWG or larger)

electric bell

electric buzzer

nails

pliers

electromagnets/relays

thumb tacks

#8 wood screws

scrap wood

Ideas for the Teacher

■ Students work in groups of 3 to 4.

■ It is possible to build a system that can both send and receive a signal that requires only three wires between stations, but this is difficult. Students will find it easier to construct a system with four wires between the stations.

■ Students should demonstrate their system by sending a message in Morse Code from one station to another, and seeing how well the receiving people decode the message.

■ Students may investigate the characteristics of electromagnetism by constructing their own electromagnets using insulated copper wire wound around a large, thick iron nail.

■ Pop cans have a film of enamel (an insulator) covering the metal to prevent aluminum from contaminating the contents. If the cans are to be used as part of an electric circuit, the enamel should be removed with sandpaper or emery cloth.

Appendices & Bibliography

Appendix A

Technical Drawings

Students should be encouraged to develop their ideas in sketch form on paper, prior to constructing their solutions. Sketches may also be made of the finished product to provide a pictorial record of the solution, along with notes on its operation. The following are a few examples of ways in which students may illustrate their ideas.

1. Pictorial Sketches

Pictorial sketches are three-dimensional diagrams of an object. Such sketches are useful for developing or demonstrating ideas.

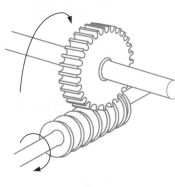

Hinge

2. Single-View Sketches

Single-view sketches are two-dimensional diagrams of an object. Each sketch focusses on one side of the object being illustrated. Usually three views (front, side, and top) are provided.

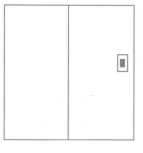

Top

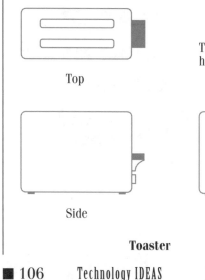

Top

Toast goes here

Side

Front

Toaster

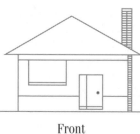

Front

Side

House

3. Storyboards

Storyboards are a series of sketches, in sequence, to show an event. They resemble a comic strip, and are useful for describing the action of a device.

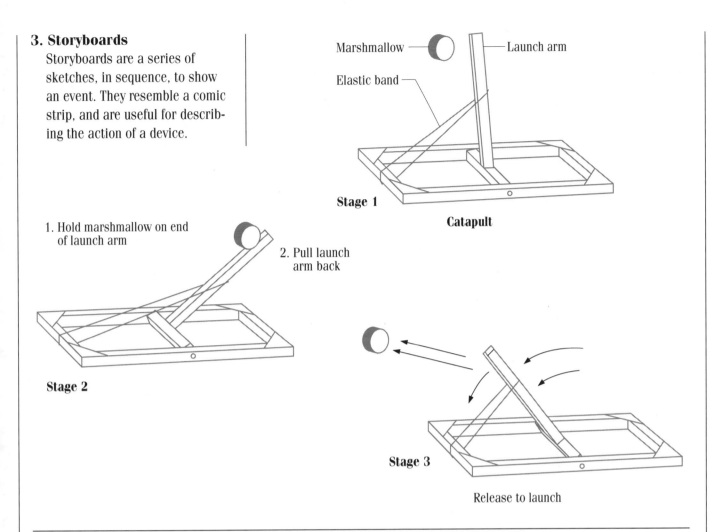

Marshmallow — Launch arm

Elastic band

Stage 1

Catapult

1. Hold marshmallow on end of launch arm

2. Pull launch arm back

Stage 2

Stage 3

Release to launch

4. Dimensioning

Dimensioning refers to numerical scale information that is added to a sketch in order to provide details about the physical size of an object and its components.

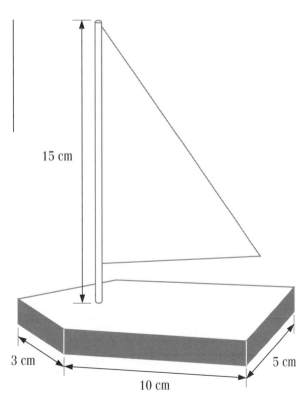

15 cm

3 cm

10 cm

5 cm

Sail Boat

Appendix B

How My Ideas Worked

Student Name(s): _____

Group or Company Name: _____

Project: _____

Sketch or Description of Solution:

What I Learned: _____

_____

_____

Possible Improvements to Solution: _____

_____

_____

_____

Appendix C

Teacher Record Sheet

Evaluating for Technological Literacy

_____ can:
(student's name)

Attitudes

Respect for Self and Others

- ❑ Maintain a clean work area.
- ❑ Clear up when work is completed.
- ❑ Use tools in a safe manner.
- ❑ Wear appropriate safety equipment.
- ❑ Share materials and equipment with others.
- ❑ Listen quietly when others are speaking.
- ❑ Share ideas with other classmates.

Inquiry and Flexibility

- ❑ Ask questions about and seek answers to problems.
- ❑ Modify solutions when unsuccessful.
- ❑ Use a variety of resources to solve problems.

Confidence

- ❑ Use tools and materials creatively while solving problems.
- ❑ Seek new processes, tools, devices, materials, etc. to solve problems outside of the scope of previous experiences.

Concern for the Environment

- ❑ Practise energy conservation techniques while working in and around the classroom.
- ❑ Employ waste reduction practices while working in and around the classroom.

Comments _____

_____

_____

_____

_____

_____

Skills

Using Tools and Materials

- ❏ Use tools safely and skillfully.
- ❏ Select appropriate materials in the solution of technological problems.
- ❏ Handle materials in a safe manner.
- ❏ Use measuring instruments appropriately.
- ❏ Use materials efficiently and with minimum waste.

Utilizing the Design Process

- ❏ Describe a variety of technological ideas to solve a given problem.
- ❏ Synthesize ideas from a number of sources into a workable solution.
- ❏ Compromise with others to reach a workable solution.
- ❏ Model and develop a variety of technological ideas to solve a given problem.
- ❏ Analyse and evaluate solution ideas.

Drawing Ability

- ❏ Present solution ideas in pictorial form.
- ❏ Illustrate a solution idea from a variety of viewpoints.
- ❏ Label sketches and diagrams appropriately.
- ❏ Describe with the aid of a sketch or diagram the operation of a solution.

Translating Drawings

- ❏ Build solutions from working drawings.
- ❏ Build stable and workable structures or mechanisms.

Construction Techniques

- ❏ Create and/or use one or more simple machines in the solution to the problem.
- ❏ Use more complex mechanisms, such as gears, motors, and hydraulic/pneumatic cylinders in the solution to the problem.

Comments _____

_____

_____

_____

_____

_____

_____

_____

_____

Knowledge

Design Process

- ❏ Describe the design process.
- ❏ Identify the needs inferred by the situation.
- ❏ Suggest solutions to the challenge.

Structures

- ❏ Identify structural elements in existing technology, such as beams, arches, domes, etc.
- ❏ Describe the function of such elements.
- ❏ Use a variety of structures in solving problems.
- ❏ Use structures appropriate for the given construction materials in the solution of problems.

Mechanisms

- ❏ Identify elements of simple machines.
- ❏ Use simple machines in solutions.
- ❏ Develop mechanisms based on simple machines.

Energy

- ❏ Identify forms of energy.
- ❏ Give examples of devices that make use of different forms of energy.
- ❏ Analyse forms of energy used in technological devices from an ecological perspective.
- ❏ Analyse forms of energy used in technological devices from an economic perspective.
- ❏ Use various forms of energy to design and build technological solutions.

Problem-Solving

- ❏ Compare the impact of existing technological solutions to common problems in terms of their impact on the environment, the economy, and society.
- ❏ Determine the extent to which technological solutions satisfy needs.
- ❏ Propose modifications and/or improvements to own solutions.
- ❏ Propose modifications and/or improvements to solutions of peers.

Comments _____

_____

_____

_____

_____

_____

_____

_____

Bibliography

Note: The ISBN numbers are provided to facilitate identification and ordering.

Anno, M. *The Earth is a Sundial*, Bodley Head, ISBN# 0-370-310-160

Baker, Susan. *Magnets*, Cherrytree, ISBN# 0-7415-5093-4

Bantock, N. Wings, *A Pop-Up Book of Things That Fly*, Random House, ISBN# 0-679-81041-2

Barrett, J. *Cloudy with a Chance of Meatballs*, Aladin Books, ISBN# 0-689-70749-5

Bingham, S. *The Ultimate Wood Block Book*, Sterling Publishing Co., Inc., ISBN# 0-8069-6662-9

Blohm, H., Beer, S. & Suzuki, D. *Pebbles to Computers*, Oxford, ISBN# 0-19-540536-6

Boyne, W.J. *The Smithsonian Book of Flight*, Macmillan Publishing Co., ISBN# 0-689-71212-X

Branley, F. *Gravity is a Mystery*, Harper, ISBN# 0-06-445057-0

Bresler, L. *Earth Facts*, Usborne, ISBN# 1-85123-1536 Science

Brown, Julie. *Inventing Things*, Gareth Stevens, ISBN# 0-8368-0035-4

Bushey, J. *Farming the Land*, Carolrhoda Books, ISBN# 0-87614-493-8

Cameron, E. *The Wonderful Flight to the Mushroom Planet*, Little, Brown, ISBN# 0-316-12540-7

Caneys, S. *Invention Book*, Workman Publishing, ISBN# 0-89480-076-0

Clement, C. *The Voice of the Wood*, Dial Publishing, ISBN# 0-8037-0635-9

Folsom, M. & Folsom, M. *The Macmillan Book of How Things Work*, Macmillan Publishing Co., 1987, ISBN# 0-689-71139-5

Green, John & Maryann Kovalski. *Junk Pile Jennifer*, North Winds Press, ISBN# 0-590-73873-9

Head, John. *The Infant Earth*, Cherrytree, ISBN# 0-7451-5011-X

Hemsley, K. *Techniques for Technology*, National Council for Educational Technology. ISBN# 1-85379-064-8

Hindley, J. *The Time Traveller Book of Knights and Castles*, Usborne Publishing Ltd., 1976, ISBN# 0-86020-068-X

Horvatic, A. *Simple Machines*, Fitzhenry & Whiteside Ltd., ISBN# 0-525-44492-0

Ingoglia, G. *The Big Book of Real Skyscrapers*, Grosset & Dunlap, ISBN# 0-448-19186-5

Ingpen, R. & Dunkle, M. *Conservation*, Macmillan, ISBN# 0-7715-9312-0

Jackson, P. *Tricks and Games with Paper*, Angus Publishing, ISBN# 9-780207-150388

Johnsey, R. *Design and Technology Through Problem Solving*, Simon & Schuster, ISBN# 0-7501-0032-X

Jonsen, G. *Monsters and Trolls*, Random House, 1977, ISBN# 0-394-83368-6

Kerrod, R. *Air in Motion*, Cherry Tree Press, ISBN # 0-7451-5026-8

Kerrod, R. *How Things Work*, Cherrytree Press Ltd., ISBN# 0-7451-5021-7

Konigsburg, E. L. *Sanuel Todd's Book of Great Inventions*, Collier Macmillan, ISBN# 0-689-31680-1

Lafferty, P. *Science In Action: Electricity and Magnetism*, Cherrytree Press Ltd., ISBN# 0-7451-5034-9

Lear, P. *Let's Look at Computers*, Hayes, ISBN# 0-88625-083-8

Lee, R. *Design Briefs*, Cambridge University Press, ISBN# 0-521-34826-9

Lee, R. *Design Briefs - Student Research Book*, Cambridge University Press, ISBN# 0-521-34827-7

Little, K. *Finding Out About Things That Fly*, Usborne Publishing Ltd., ISBN# 1-85123-205-2

Little, K. *Things On Wheels*, Usborne Publishing Ltd., ISBN# 1-85123191-9

Macaulay, D. *Castle*, Houghton Mifflin, ISBN# 0-385-32920-5

Macaulay, D. *The Way Things Work*, Houghton Mifflin, ISBN # 0-395-42857-2

Macaulay, D. *Unbuilding*, Houghton Mifflin, ISBN# 0-395-45425-5

McNeil, Mary Jean. *How Things Began*, Usborne & Hayes

Morris, C. *Advanced Paper Aircraft Construction Mk.II*, Angus Publishing, ISBN# 9780207 154553

Morris, C. *Advanced Paper Aircraft Construction Mk.III*, Angus Publishing, ISBN# 0-200-14964X

Neville, E. C. *The Bridge*, Harper & Row Junior Books, ISBN# 0-06-024385-6

Richards, R. *An Early Start To Technology*, Simon & Schuster, ISBN# 0-7501-0033-8

Rowlands, D. *Problem-Solving in Science and Technology - Teachers' Manual*, Hutchinson Education, ISBN# 0-09-172761-8

Royston, A. & Thompson G. *Monster Building Machines*, Barrons, ISBN# 0-8120-6174-8

Scott, S. *Living Without Electricity*, Good Books, ISBN# 0-934672-61-X

Scrine, R.V. & Clewes, E. *First Technology*, Hodder and Stoughton, ISBN# 0-340-41159-7

Shooter, K. *Making Things Work*, Cambridge University Press, ISBN# 0-521-339707

Turner, Ann. *Heron Street*, Harper, ISBN# 0-06-026184-6

Vowels, A. & Mackie, D. *Robotics*, Hayes, ISBN# 0-88625-113-3

Wagner, J. *The Machine at the Heart of the World*, Kestrell Books, ISBN# 0-7226-64826

Ward, A. *Experimenting with Sound*, Dryad Press Ltd., ISBN# 0-8521-9662-8

Webb, A. *Talk About Sand*, Watts, ISBN# 0-531-10370-6

Weiss, H. *Shelters From Tepee to Igloo*, Crowell, ISBN# 0-690-04553-0

Williams, J. *Flight*, Wayland, ISBN# 0-7502-0026-X

Williams, J. *Machines*, Wayland, ISBN# 0-7502-0025-1

Wilson, F. *What it Feels Like to be a Building*, Doubleday and Co., ISBN# 0-89133-142-5

Wyatt, V. *Inventions*, Greey de Pencier, ISBN# 0-920775-21-7

Wyler, R. *Science Fun With Toy Boats and Planes*, Messner, ISBN# 0-671-62453-9

Wyler, R. *Science Fun With Toy Cars and Trucks*, Messner, ISBN# 0-671-65854-9

Yarwood, A. & Orme, A.H. *Design and Technology*, Hodder and Stoughton, ISBN# 0-340-32975-0

Zubrowski, B. *Clocks*, Wm. Morrow, ISBN# 0-688-06925-8

Zubrowski, B. *Raceways*, Wm. Morrow, ISBN# 0-688-04160-4

Zubrowski, B. *Water Pumps and Siphons*, Little, Brown, ISBN# 0-316-98877-4

Zubrowski, B. *Wheels At Work*, Wm. Morrow, ISBN# 0-688-06349-7

Ideas for Egg Races & Other Practical Problem Solving Activities, British Association for the Advancement of Science, 1983.

More Ideas for Egg Races & Other Practical Problem Solving Activities, British Association for the Advancement of Science, 1985.